GCSE

HIGHER LEVEL AND EXTENSION
MATHEMATICS

GUIDES

Brian Speed

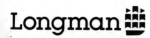
Longman

LONGMAN REVISE GUIDES

Series editors: Geoff Black and Stuart Wall

TITLES AVAILABLE:
Art and Design
Biology
British and European History
Business Studies
C.D.T. – Design and Realisation
C.D.T. – Technology
Chemistry
Computer Studies
Economics
English
English Literature
French
Geography
German
Home Economics
Integrated Humanities
Mathematics
Mathematics: Higher Level and Extension
Music
Physics
Religious Studies
Science
Social and Economic History
Typewriting and Keyboarding Applications
World History

Longman Group UK Limited,
Longman House, Burnt Mill, Harlow,
Essex CM20 2JE, England
and Associated Companies throughout the world.

First published 1989
3rd impression 1991

British Library Cataloguing in Publication Data

Speed, Brian
  GCSE higher and extension mathematics.
  1. England. Secondary schools. Curriculum subjects: Mathematics.
  GCSE examinations.
  I. Title
  510′.76

  ISBN 0–582–04033–7

Produced by The Pen and Ink Book Company,
Huntingdon, Cambridgeshire

Set in 10/12pt Century Old Style

Produced by Longman Singapore Publishers Pte Ltd
Printed in Singapore

CONTENTS

EDITORS' PREFACE

Longman Revise Guides are written by experienced examiners and teachers, and aim to give you the best possible foundation for success in examinations and other modes of assessment. Examiners are well aware that the performance of many candidates falls well short of their true potential, and this series of books aims to remedy this, by encouraging thorough study and a full understanding of the concepts involved. The Revise Guides should be seen as course companions and study aids to be used throughout the year, not just for last minute revision.

Examiners are in no doubt that a structured approach in preparing for examinations and in presenting coursework can, together with hard work and diligent application, substantially improve performance.

The largely self-contained nature of each chapter gives the book a useful degree of flexibility. After starting with the opening general chapters on the background to the GCSE, and the syllabus coverage, all other chapters can be read selectively, in any order appropriate to the stage you have reached in your course.

We believe that this book, and the series as a whole, will help you establish a solid platform of basic knowledge and examination technique on which to build.

Geoff Black and Stuart Wall

ACKNOWLEDGEMENTS

I would like to thank the following people for their contributions to the production of this book: Geoff Black and Stuart Wall for their efficient editing and encouragement; Terry Mullen for sharing his thoughts and insights during the preparation of the book; my pupils at Pope Pius X School for their constant inspiration and questioning that has helped to make this book relevant to GCSE students at large; my mother, Mrs Elsie Speed for her dedication to the typewriter and to finding spelling corrections; Gillian my wife who has now learnt to cope with my working into the early hours; and finally to my lads, James, John and Joseph who found an alternative sport to 'Dad baiting' for a while.

I am also indebted to the following Examination Boards for giving me permission to use some of their GCSE questions in this book.

London and East Anglian Examining Group (LEAG)
Midland Examining Group (MEG)
Northern Examining Association (NEA)
Northern Ireland Schools Examinations Council (NISEC)
Oxford and Cambridge Schools Examination Board (O and C)
Welsh Joint Education Committee (WJEC)

The above groups do not accept any responsibility for the answers I have given to their questions. All suggestions and any mistakes in the answers are entirely my responsibility. I would be most grateful to any reader who informs me of any errors should they occur.

Brian Speed

The publishers are grateful to the following schools and colleges for their co-operation:

Bishop Fox's School, Taunton; Chase High School, Malvern; Derby Tertiary College, Mackworth; Impington Village College, Cambridge; Poole Grammar School; Pope Pius Comprehensive School, Rotherham; Queensbury School, Bradford; Rugby School; St Helena School, Chesterfield; St Christopher School, Letchworth; St Mary's High School, Cheshunt; Shildon Sunnydale Comprehensive School; Sir William Perkins's School, Chertsey; South Park Sixth Form College, Middlesbrough; Thrybergh Comprehensive School, Rotherham; Waddesdon Church of England Secondary School, Aylesbury; Wollaston School, Wellingborough.

HIGHER LEVEL AND EXTENSION MATHEMATICS

GETTING STARTED

GCSE mathematics is at present unique in that it allows three levels of entry; basic, intermediate and higher. The higher level is intended *only* for those candidates who stand a reasonable chance of gaining a grade A or B.

If the highest grade you expect to gain is a C, then you should enter for the intermediate level, as there you will have the best chance to show what you can do. This book is written specifically for those entering the *higher level* and aiming to obtain grade A or B. It is also written for those candidates taking an *extension* paper for their examination. This first chapter considers the different requirements and details from the various examination boards. (If you are entering for intermediate or basic level then you should refer to the Longman Revise Guide "Mathematics".

INTRODUCING HIGHER MATHEMATICS

1 ▷ HIGHER LEVEL OF ENTRY

The target grades at this level are A, B and C. A grade D can however be awarded, but if you do not achieve this standard then you will be unclassified.

As has already been noted, you should only be entered for this level if there is a *realistic chance* of your gaining a grade A or B. If this is so and you have a bad day, then you should still end up with a grade C. If you gain a grade D or, worse still, if you are unclassified, then it will indicate that you were incorrectly entered. Unless a major change occurs in your learning or circumstances, then when you *next* take the exam you would be well advised to take the intermediate level examination.

2 ▷ EXTENSION PAPER

Some examination boards accept that there are a number of candidates who need a still greater challenge in their mathematics examination than that posed by the hardest paper set at the Higher Level. They do this by giving able candidates the opportunity to sit an *extension paper* in addition to the two papers set at the Higher Level. The *syllabus* for this may be slightly extended, and the *questions* themselves will certainly be far more searching. If this paper is passed then although the candidate can receive no higher than a grade A, the GCSE certificate will indicate that you have passed the extension paper in Mathematics. If you fail this paper, then no mention is made of your attempt to pass it.

3 ▷ COURSEWORK

This is optional until 1991, when all mathematics syllabuses will have to include it. You will be informed by your teacher at school or college as to whether coursework is to be included in your final grade. The majority of this book will be devoted to the written, timed, end of course examination papers, but Chapter 2 considers coursework and the best ways of dealing with it.

4 ▷ SCHEMES OF ASSESSMENT

LONDON AND EAST ANGLIAN GROUP (LEAG)

Syllabus A (no coursework up to 1990)
Level X (basic)   will sit Paper 1 and Paper 2
Level Y (intermediate)   will sit Paper 2 and Paper 3
Level Z (higher)   will sit Paper 3 and Paper 4

There is no choice of questions on each paper, and each paper is worth 50% of the final total.

Syllabus B
The papers are set as above, but coursework is now included. Each paper is worth 35% and the coursework is worth 30%. The coursework will consist of a mental test worth 5% and five set tasks, each of 5%, give the other 25%.

Syllabus SMP (no coursework up to 1990)
The papers are set as for Syllabus A, with no coursework and with each paper worth 50%.

NORTHERN EXAMINING ASSOCIATION (NEA)

Syllabuses A and B
Both include an optional coursework component (until 1991 when it will be compulsory).

Scheme I (with no coursework)
Level P (basic)   will sit Paper 1 and Paper 2 (both 50%)
Level Q (intermediate)   will sit Paper 2 (45%) and Paper 3 (55%)
Level R (higher)   will sit Paper 3 (45%) and Paper 4 (55%)

There is no choice of questions on any of the papers.

Scheme II

There is coursework worth 25% of the assessment. The combination of written papers is the same as above, but:

Level P – both 37½%
Level Q – Paper 2, 33%; Paper 3, 42%
Level R – Paper 3, 33%; Paper 4, 42%

Syllabus C

This has compulsory coursework worth 25%, with the combination of papers the same as for Syllabuses A and B, but the weightings are:

Level P – both 37½%
Level Q – Paper 2, 34%; Paper 3, 41%
Level R – Paper 3, 34%; Paper 4, 41%

MIDLAND EXAMINING GROUP (MEG)

Syllabus Mathematics

Has an optional coursework component until 1991, after which coursework will be compulsory.

Scheme I (with no coursework)

Each level will take two papers, both worth 50%. The first paper will be short-answer questions, all answered on the question paper, and no choice. The second paper contains longer structured questions and offers choice in section B at the intermediate and the higher levels. The intermediate choice is 4 out of 5 questions. The higher choice is 4 out of 6 questions. At the foundation (lower) level, the answers will be written on the question paper, and at the intermediate and higher levels they will be written on separate script paper.

Scheme II (with coursework worth 25%)

The papers are the same as for Scheme I, but the weightings are now: first paper 50%; second paper 25%. The coursework assignment will be the candidate's choice of five assignments arranged with the school or college.

Syllabus Mathematics (mature)

The type of papers and choice is the same as for the syllabus 'mathematics'. Candidates take two papers suitable for their level, with the weightings being: first paper, 40%; second paper, 50%. However, for the 'mature' syllabus there is an aural test giving the other 10%. The aural test will be 20 questions, to be answered on an answer sheet provided. You are **NOT** allowed to use a calculator in the aural test.

Syllabus Mathematics (SMP (11–16))

There will be three parts to the assessment scheme at each level:
a)   Written papers
     Foundation level   Paper 1 and Paper 2, 35% each
     Intermediate level   Paper 2 and Paper 3, 35% each
     Higher level   Paper 3 and Paper 4, 35% each
b)   Coursework, giving 25%, consisting of eight tasks provided by the Examination Board.
c)   Aural test, giving 5%. This will consist of two tests given orally from questions provided by the Examination Board.

Syllabus Mathematics (SMP) (until 1991)

There is no coursework component, and the combination of papers is exactly the same as for the syllabus SMP (11–16), except that the weightings will be 50% for each paper. Candidates will be required to attempt all questions, except in Paper 4, section B, where there will be a choice of 4 out of 6 questions.

SOUTHERN EXAMINING GROUP (SEG)

There are two schemes, one with coursework and one (until 1991) with no coursework.

Scheme I (with no coursework)
This consists of two parts:
a)   Level 1 (basic)   will sit Paper 1 and Paper 2 (45% each)
     Level 2 (intermediate)   will sit Paper 2 and Paper 3 (45% each)
     Level 3 (higher)   will sit Paper 3 and Paper 4 (45% each)
There is no choice of questions on any of the papers.
b)   Aural tests giving 10%. Each candidate will take two 15-minute aural tests as:
     Level 1 (basic)   Aural tests 1 and 2
     Level 2 (intermediate)   Aural tests 2 and 3
     Level 3 (higher)   Aural tests 3 and 4

Calculators are **NOT** allowed to be used for the Aural tests.

Scheme II (with coursework)
This consists of three parts:
a)   The written papers are the same combinations as above, but the weightings are now 25% each.
b)   The aural tests as above give 10%.
c)   The coursework, or 'centre-based assessment' as it is called in the syllabus, gives 40%. This will consist of three units, which will be arranged by you and your school or college.

WELSH JOINT EDUCATION COMMITTEE (WJEC)

There are two schemes, one with coursework and one without.

Scheme A (with coursework)
This will consist of two parts, written papers and coursework, with weightings in the ratio of 200:70.
a)   The written papers each earn 100 marks and are taken as:
     Level 1 (basic)   will sit Paper 1 and Paper 2
     Level 2 (intermediate)   will sit Paper 2 and Paper 3
     Level 3 (higher)   will sit Paper 3 and Paper 4
b)   The coursework will consist of two tasks provided by the Examination Board, and combined to give 70 marks.

Scheme B (without coursework)
The written papers will be taken as in Scheme A and each one is worth 50%. There is no choice of questions on any paper.

NORTHERN IRELAND SCHOOLS EXAMINATIONS COUNCIL (NISEC)

There are two syllabuses A and B. The syllabus content and the written papers are identical in each case, the only difference being that syllabus B has no coursework included in the assessment.

Syllabus A
There are *three* parts to the assessment of Syllabus A at each level.
a)   Written papers
     At each level you sit *two written papers*, each of which will consist of *short answer* questions and *long questions* (most of which will be *structured*). There is no choice of question offered. Each paper is worth 35% of the final assessment.
b)   Aural and computation
     There will also be an aural and computation test, which is set for each level. This will test your mental arithmetic and how well you can understand a spoken instruction regarding information available on a separate document. This test is worth 10% of the assessment.
c)   Coursework
     You will normally have to hand in *four* assignments for assessing. Your teacher will tell you what these assignments are. They could include work on topics such as practical geometry, measurement, statistics, everyday application of mathematics and investigations. This coursework element is worth 20% of the assessment.

Syllabus B

The same as syllabus A *except* that there is no coursework to include. The combinations are therefore different and as follows:

a)   the two written papers are each worth 45% of the assessment.

b)   the aural and computation test is worth 10% of the assessment.

INTERNATIONAL GENERAL CERTIFICATE OF SECONDARY EDUCATION (IGCSE)

This syllabus has been designed to meet international mathematical needs while being based on the United Kingdom's *national criteria* as published by the SEAC.

There are only *two* levels available: the basic level being included in the *lower level* of the two which is called the *core curriculum* where the only grades available are C to G; the *higher level* being called the *extended curriculum*, where the only available grades are from A to E. There is also an *optional* coursework element in place of part of the written papers. The assessment will be in *three* parts:

a)   a *written* paper of *short answer* questions.

b)   a *written* paper of *structured questions*.

c)   a *written* paper of *problems* **or** the *school based assessment*.

There is *no* choice of question on any paper. The combination of the different parts of the assessment are:

core:	a)	first paper	35%
	b)	second paper	40%
	c)	third part	25%
extended:	a)	first paper	37.5%
	b)	second paper	37.5%
	c)	third part	25%

The *school based assessment* which is *optional* consists of four coursework assignments (20%) and two aural tests (5%). The four coursework assignments will be on the four areas of:

■   statistics and/or probability

■   geometry

■   investigations

■   practical applications of mathematics.

The aural tests will be about fifteen minutes of single response questions aimed at each different level.

You may use a suitable calculator in each part of the assessment and, if you wish, four figure tables also. For centres that are in areas where electronic calculators are not readily and cheaply obtainable, there is an alternative version of the examination available.

HIGHER AND EXTENSION MATHEMATICS

5 ›   ASSUMED KNOWLEDGE

Since this book is aiming only at the higher level, it will be assumed that you have a basic knowledge of mathematics already. In this chapter we list this *assumed* knowledge, and indicate the *mathematical content* of the *higher level* for the different examination boards. You need to check this part of the chapter for yourself to see exactly which topics do relate to you.

Number	Different types of number, eg. integers, odd, even, prime, multiples, factors, irrationals, rationals, prime factors, sequences, standard form, squares and square roots.
Fractions	Vulgar and decimal with the four rules. Conversion from vulgar to decimal and vice versa. Percentage and its uses.

Directed number	The four rules of.
Approximation	Rounding off to significant figures and decimal places.
Household finance	Simple and compound interest, taxation, loans, wages and salaries.
Tables and Charts	Being able to read them as well as construct them.
Ratio	Scale factors, best buys, scale drawing. Proportion, both direct and inverse. Speed, and foreign currency exchange rates.
Formulae	Flowcharts, use of simple equations, transposition of.
Algebra	Factors, simplification, simple linear equations and in-equalities.
Indices	Integral, both positive and negative.
Co-ordinates	Plotting points and drawing graphs from given data.
Graphs	Interpreting different types of graphs, such as travel graphs and conversion graphs. Gradients as found from a graph. Solution of simultaneous, linear equations by a graph.
Angles	In triangles, parallels, polygons, and in semicircles.
Plane figures	Properties of triangles, quadrilaterals, circles and polygons.
Symmetry	Line and rotational
Solid figures	Their names and their nets.
Congruency and similarity	
Perimeter	Of plane figures and circles.
Area	Of rectangles, triangles, parallelograms and circles.
Volume	Of cuboids, cylinders and prisms.
Trigonometry	Simple right angled triangles.
Pythagoras	As used to solve right angled triangles.
Constructions	Triangles, rectangles and quadrilaterals from given data. Bisector of lines and angles.
Scale drawings	And when to use them.
Bearings	Compass points and bearings from one point to another.
Transformation geometry	Tessellations, reflections, simple enlargements, rotations of 90° and 180°, and translations.
Statistics	Bar charts, equal width histograms, pictograms and pie charts.
Frequency distributions	And their use in constructing charts, with also the use of grouped data. Scatter diagrams.
Averages	Mean, mode and median.
Probability	Simple, equally likely situations and combined events.

6 ▷ HIGHER LEVEL

The Higher Level of mathematics does differ from exam board to exam board, and from syllabus to syllabus, so you do need to take note of the differences and to think how they will affect you. The table below will guide you on which parts of the book are relevant to *your* Higher Level syllabus.

The *Higher Level* is referred to by the different boards as:

LEAG	Level Z
NEA	Level R
MEG	Higher
SEG	Level 3
WJEC	Level 3
NISEC	High
IGCSE	Extended

Chapter and topic	LEAG			NEA			MEG				SEG	WJEC	NISEC	IGCSE
	A	B	SMP	A	B	C	Maths	Mature	SMP (11–16)	SMP				
3 Sets and Venn Diagrams	✓	✓		✓	✓	✓					✓	✓		✓
4 Percentage, Compound interest				✓	✓	✓	✓	✓					✓	
5 Number Patterns	✓	✓	✓	✓	✓	✓	✓	✓	✓	✓	✓	✓	✓	✓
6 Ratios of similar shapes	✓	✓		✓	✓	✓	✓	✓	✓	✓	✓	✓	✓	✓
Direct, inverse and joint proportion	✓	✓	✓	✓	✓	✓		✓	✓	✓	✓	✓	✓	✓
7 Quadratic factorization, equations	✓	✓	✓	✓	✓	✓	✓	✓	✓	✓	✓	✓	✓	✓
Simultaneous equations	✓	✓		✓	✓	✓	✓	✓	✓	✓	✓	✓		✓
Algebraic fractions						✓	✓	✓	✓					
Fractional indices				✓			✓	✓	✓		✓	✓	✓	✓
Functions and their combinations			✓	✓	✓	✓			✓	✓	✓	✓		
8 Drawing graphs of inequalities				✓	✓		✓		✓	✓	✓		✓	
Drawing graphs of simultaneous equations	✓	✓	✓	✓	✓	✓	✓	✓	✓	✓	✓	✓		✓
Area under a graph	✓	✓		✓	✓	✓	✓	✓			✓			
Gradients and their uses	✓	✓	✓	✓	✓	✓	✓	✓			✓	✓	✓	✓
9 Cyclic quadrilaterals	✓	✓		✓							✓	✓		
Angles in a circle	✓	✓	✓	✓							✓	✓	✓	✓
Axes and planes of symmetry	✓	✓		✓							✓			
Intersecting chord theorem	✓	✓												
Loci			✓	✓						✓	✓			
10 Length of arc, area of sector	✓	✓		✓	✓	✓	✓	✓	✓	✓			✓	✓
Area of trapezium	✓	✓	✓	✓	✓	✓	✓	✓	✓	✓	✓	✓	✓	✓
Area using sine rule (½ a.b. sin C)							✓	✓				✓		✓
Volume of prisms, spheres and cones	✓	✓		✓	✓	✓	✓	✓	✓	✓	✓	✓	✓	✓
Surface areas	✓	✓		✓	✓		✓	✓	✓	✓	✓	✓	✓	✓
3D solutions using trigonometry and Pythagoras	✓	✓	✓	✓	✓	✓	✓	✓	✓	✓	✓	✓	✓	✓
Sine and Cosine rule							✓	✓				✓		✓
Latitude and longitude								✓						
11 Vectors	✓	✓	✓	✓	✓	✓	✓	✓	✓		✓	✓		✓
Matrices	✓	✓	✓	✓	✓		✓		✓	✓				✓
Transformations and combinations of	✓	✓	✓	✓	✓		✓		✓	✓			✓	✓
Enlargements with negative or fraction scale factors	✓	✓	✓	✓	✓		✓				✓		✓	✓
12 Cumulative frequency				✓	✓	✓	✓	✓	✓	✓			✓	✓
Unequal width histograms				✓		✓	✓							✓
Probabilities (and/or)	✓	✓		✓	✓	✓			✓	✓	✓		✓	

7 > EXTENSION SYLLABUS

This is different for the different boards; some simply ask more searching questions on the *same* Higher Level syllabus, while others will include *extra topics*. These syllabuses are developing and changing year by year at the moment, so any printing would very soon be out of date and of no use to you. Ask your teacher what topics you need to cover; they will be included at various points in this book. Alternatively, contact your own Examination Board. The addresses are listed below. You can write and request an order form to purchase your own copy of the syllabus. You will then have to complete the order form and enclose the cost of the syllabus and postage.

8 > ADDRESSES OF THE EXAMINATION BOARDS

London and East Anglian Group (LEAG)
London   University of London Schools Examinations Board
             Stewart House, 32 Russell Square, London WC1B 5DN
LREB   London Regional Examinations Board
             Lyon House, 104 Wandsworth High Street, London SW18 4LF
EAEB   East Anglian Examinations Board
             The Lindens, Lexden Road, Colchester, Essex CO3 3RL

Northern Examining Association (NEA)
JMB   Joint Matriculation Board
             Devas Street, Manchester M15 6EU
ALSEB   Associated Lancashire Schools Examining Board
             12 Harter Street, Manchester M1 6HL
NREB   North Regional Examinations Board
             Wheatfield Road, Westerhop, Newcastle upon Tyne NE5 5JZ
NWREB   North-West Regional Examinations Board
             Orbit House, Albert Street, Eccles, Manchester M30 0WL
YHREB   Yorkshire and Humberside Regional Examinations Board
             Harrogate Office – 21–33 Springfield Avenue, Harrogate HG1 2HW
             Sheffield Office – Scarsdale House, 136 Derbyshire Lane, Sheffield S8 8SE

Midland Examining Group (MEG)
Cambridge University of Cambridge Local Examinations Syndicate
             Syndicate Buildings, 1 Hills Road, Cambridge CB1 2EU
O & C   Oxford and Cambridge Schools Examinations Board
             10 Trumpington Street, Cambridge CB2 1QB, and Elsfield Way, Oxford OX2 8EP
SUJB   Southern Universities' Joint Board for School Examinations
             Cotham Road, Bristol BS6 6DD
WMEB   West Midlands Examinations Board
             Norfolk House, Smallbrook Queensway, Birmingham B5 4NJ
EMREB   East Midlands Regional Examinations Board
             Robins Wood House, Robins Wood Road, Aspley, Nottingham NG8 3NR

Southern Examining Group (SEG)
AEB   The Associated Examining Board
             Stag Hill House, Guildford, Surrey GU2 5XJ
Oxford   Oxford Delegacy of Local Examinations
             Ewert Place, Summertown, Oxford OX2 7BZ
SREB   Southern Regional Examinations Board
             Avondale House, 33 Carlton Crescent, Southampton, S9 4YL
SEREB   South-East Regional Examinations Board
             Beloe House, 2–10 Mount Ephraim Road, Tonbridge TN1 1EU
SWEB   South-Western Examinations Board
             23–29 Marsh Street, Bristol BS1 4BP

Northern Ireland Schools Examinations Council (NISEC)
             Beechill House, 42 Beechill Road, Belfast BT8 4RS

Welsh Joint Education Committee (WJEC)
             245 Western Avenue, Cardiff CF5 2YX

International GCSE (IGCSE)
             University of Cambridge Local Examinations Syndicate
             1 Hills Road, Cambridge CB12 2EU

EXAMINATION AND ASSESSMENT TECHNIQUES

CALCULATORS

FORMULAE LIST

REVISION

EXAMINATION ROOM STRATEGY

EXAMINATION EQUIPMENT

EXAMINATION QUESTIONS

THE EXAMINATIONS

It is encouraging to know that if you *have been correctly entered* for the higher level of mathematics then you can do *at least half* of the examination questions well. This should give you a lot of confidence before you go into the examination. Being confident is helpful, since being anxious often means that students make careless mistakes.

1 > CALCULATORS

All GCSE examinations allow you to have your calculator available. The questions will be set on the assumption that you have a calculator suitable to your level. For example, you will be asked some *trigonometry questions* at this high level, so make sure that you have a *scientific* calculator. It is up to **YOU** to be responsible for your calculator and not the exam board, school or college. Do have the right one, and make certain that the batteries are not going to run out on you (perhaps take some spares). Do use a calculator that you are familiar with, and not a strange one borrowed at the last minute.

When using the calculator in the examination, do not forget to *write out* your method of solution, otherwise you will often lose marks. In marking a recent exam paper the answer to one question should have been £1.99. Some candidates gave the answer as £1.98 with *no* working out, so they got no marks at all, even though it is quite likely that they *knew* what they were doing, but had just made a small error, perhaps in rounding off. You will throw marks away if you fail to put down your *method of solution*. Make sure you are familiar with the standard form notation on your calculator and how to use this with large or very small numbers. This is covered in chapter 5 of this book.

2 > FORMULAE LIST

Each Examination Board will supply a formulae list for each syllabus, and for each level in that syllabus. You are advised to become familiar with this list, so that you know where to find the formulae when needed. It is also important that you practise using those formulae. If you have practised using the formulae *before* the exam, then this will give you confidence in using them in the examination itself.

3 > REVISION

There is of course no substitute for hard work *throughout* the course, and for regularly doing homework and classwork assignments. Revision is, however, important and should be started well before the examination, best of all *before* the Easter holiday leading to the examination. The best way to revise mathematics is to *do* it. You should try as many questions as you can beforehand, this is why there are a lot of questions at the end of each chapter. Do not be afraid of going through the same question more than once during your revision. This will be helpful practice in using the correct technique for answering that type of question, and it should help boost your confidence. Do not revise for too long at a single sitting! You are advised to revise in short periods of between 45 to 60 minutes then to have a break before doing any more. Of course, this will vary with individuals but, if you've started your revision early enough, this is usually the best way rather than a last final fling!

Use this book to remind you of the things you have been taught. Go through the *worked examples*; then try the *exercises* for yourself, *checking* the answer before going any further. Finally, try the *exam questions* at the end of each chapter, making sure that you put down all your working out, just as you will have to do in the examination itself.

4 > EXAMINATION ROOM STRATEGY

Remember, you can do *at least half* the questions, and there will always be some that cause problems. You must use your time properly, so do not waste it. The majority of GCSE examinations use 'Question and Answer Books', which means that there is space for you to work out your answer and to give an answer on the exam paper itself. So it doesn't matter in what *order* you do the questions. Go through the paper and answer the questions *you can do* first, then go back and attempt the ones you've left out. If a question causes you particular problems and you cannot see what to do, then leave it, go on to another and come back to it later. In other words, 'do what you can do well' first. This will help you to 'put marks into the bank' and will help you to gain confidence before you tackle the more 'difficult' questions.

The *extension papers* will not use question and answer booklets; rather you will receive just a set of questions. You are not usually expected to answer them all, but have a free choice to do those which you want to. It is better to do a few *complete* questions rather than lots of bits of questions here and there. So look through the paper and find a few questions that look 'interesting' to you; that is to say, that you can follow what they are saying and asking you to do. Do these first, and try to complete all parts of them. The extension paper is being used to see which candidates can *sustain* a piece of mathematics right through a problem and not give up half way through. So, again, the same advice as for the question and answer book type papers, 'do what you can do well' first, then look elsewhere, but in the questions you *do* attempt, try to complete each part of the question.

Most examination papers will tell you *how many marks* are available to a question; the more difficult a question is, the more marks are generally given to it. So if you come across a question worth 5 marks and one worth 2 marks, you should expect the 2 mark question to be answered more easily than the 5 mark question. If you have managed to do the 5 mark question very easily, perhaps more easily than the 2 mark question, just check that you have in fact done the question that *has been set* and have not misread it!

If you're answering on an answer booklet, do also use the *number of lines* left for your answer as a guide to the amount you should write. If there is only one line left for working, then you should not need to do a lot of working out. If, however, five lines have been left for working, then you should expect to need to complete a number of stages to get to the answer.

The number of marks per question will also give you some idea of how much *time* to spend on each question. Suppose an examination paper lasts 2½ hours (150 minutes) and there are 100 marks, then each mark has an average time of 1½ minutes, and hence a five mark question should not take more than 8 minutes. Of course you should perhaps allow 10 minutes at the start of the exam for reading through the paper (or booklet) carefully and for choosing your early questions, and perhaps 10 minutes for checking at the end. In this case you would be able to use the 'rule of thumb' that you have just over one minute per mark. Working out the *minutes per mark* should not be taken *too* far, but it does give you some idea on how to use your time well in the examination.

Finally, do not forget to *check* those answers, especially the sense and the accuracy of your answer. If you have calculated the cost of a car to be £6, you ought to suspect that your answer is wrong and check it. Year after year examiners always mark papers where 'stupid' answers are given, such as a man being paid a salary of £45 a year! Do check your answers, it will gain you marks. Also, check that you have *rounded off* suitably. Many questions will say 'round your answer to 1 decimal place', etc., in which case you could obtain marks for rounding off. But other questions might simply say 'calculate the distance . . .', and if your answer is something like 8.273419 km, you are quite likely to lose a mark for your answer since it is not given to a suitable degree of accuracy. You must round off sensibly or be prepared to lose marks.

You ought to be doing many of these checks whilst answering the question the first time, but do go through the routine as a check at the end. It may be boring, but if it gains you a number of marks you would otherwise lose, and this makes the difference between grades, it will have been well worth doing.

5 > EXAMINATION EQUIPMENT

You will be required to calculate, draw and construct. You must therefore have the right equipment for the job. Do not rely on the school providing it, since if you provide the equipment you are familiar with, you can be more confident that you can use it and rely on it. Make certain you have the following:

calculator	pencil sharpener
batteries for calculator	rubber
ruler	protractor
sharp pencils	pair of compasses
pen (and a spare pen)	set square

6 > EXAMINATION QUESTIONS

There are different *types* of question that you could meet: eg. multiple choice, short answer, structured and combination.

MULTIPLE CHOICE

A *multiple choice* question is a short question with four or five different answers from which to choose the right one. The way to answer these questions is to actually *do* the question and then to see if your answer matches one of those given. If not, then you know that you've gone wrong and must look again. Do not be tempted to guess at the most obvious answer straight away, but do work it out. If, at the end of the examination, you have failed to complete some of these multiple choice questions, then it is legitimate to have an 'intelligent guess' at the answers (but this should always be the last resort). Only the LEAG use this type of question at the moment, and this is just part of their paper 3.

Example 1

$2(3x - 5) - 3(x - 2) =$

A $3x - 16$ C $3x - 7$ E $3x - 3$

B $3x - 12$ D $3x - 4$ (LEAG; 1988)

Here you would do the question first by multiplying out, then by simplifying to $3x - 4$; then check that the answer found *is* one of those given (here D).

SHORT-ANSWER QUESTIONS

This type of question is usually given one or two marks, and you may only have a line or two on which to answer the question. You must first assess what you have to do, then be sure to write down the *method* you are using as well as the answer, suitably rounded off.

Example 2

Find the value of x such that $90 < x < 180$ and $\sin x° = 0.4567$ (NEA; 1988)

Here you need to notice that the answer you want is between 90 and 180, hence the calculator answer to 0.4567 [INV] [SIN] which gives 27.17 (rounded off), needs to be taken away from 180, hence $180 - 27.17 = 152.83$ should be written down. If you showed no method of solution here, and wrote an incorrectly rounded answer of 152.9° only, then you are likely to gain no marks at all.

STRUCTURED QUESTIONS

These are the longer questions that will use one answer *as part of the next question*. This may occur perhaps two or three times in the one question. It is also vital that you show *all* your method of solution here, as one wrong answer early on could make all subsequent answers wrong. To gain marks you must show exactly what you have done.

Example 3

Karl won £2000 in a competition and put it into a Building Society account that paid him 5% interest every 6 months. How much will he have in the account after:

a) 6 months?

b) 1 year?   (NEA; 1988)

c) 2 years?

You can see how you use the answer to part a) to find the answer to part b) and then this answer to find the final answer to part c), and that any mistakes made earlier will make a wrong answer appear later . . . so it is vital that you show all your method of solution in each section of the question. If you did this question correctly, then you would find that your final answer to part c) was £2431.0125, which should be rounded off to give £2431 or £2431.01.

COMBINATION QUESTIONS

A longer question is often a *combination* of short answer and structured questions.

Example 4

A fruit cake is a cylinder of height 7 cm and radius 9 cm. It is to have its top and sides covered in marzipan.

a)   i) The top covering is 0.7 cm thick. Calculate this volume of marzipan.

       ii) A strip of marzipan 7.7 cm wide is to be wrapped round the side of the cake. Show that it must be about 57 cm long.

      iii) This strip is 0.5 cm thick. Calculate the volume of marzipan needed for the whole cake.

b)   A family baker makes 12 such cakes. He buys marzipan in 500 g packs. Each pack has a volume of 180 cm³. How many packs will he need to cover the 12 cakes?

                                                                        (MEG; 1988)

You should set out the parts a) i) and ii) as short answer questions, with your method clearly stated. The final part a) iii) is done by combining the answer to part a) i) with information in part ii) to find the total volume of marzipan. Then the final answer to part b) is calculated by multiplying the volume of one cake (396 cm³) found in part a), by 12, then dividing by 180 to give 26.4. Hence the baker needs to buy 27 packs of marzipan.

These answers must be clearly written down, since it is possible for you to have made a mistake in one of the earlier parts and the examiner marking your paper needs to be able to see what *you* have done, rather than have to do your calculation *himself* as a means of checking what you really have done!

SUMMARY

To summarise this section we can simply say that at all stages you should show the method of solution, unless you are certain that there is only one mark for the question and that no method is being looked for.

COURSEWORK

It is the intention that *coursework* should be an important part of the assessment (see chapter 1), so it is important that your assignments be well planned throughout the course and that they do not become an unwelcome burden at the end of the course.

Your school or college will be responsible for deciding upon the actual nature of the coursework and the way in which it is organised. There are many different tasks you could be asked to do. Whatever the nature of the coursework, the assessment will be made in three main areas: *Practical, Investigation,* and *Extended.*

1 PRACTICAL WORK

You will be assessed on:

a) How you planned the task, how you carried it out and how accurate you were. Evidence of these three stages is necessary.
b) Whether you have demonstrated that you understand the use of equipment. For example in weighing, that you have used an appropriate set of scales.
c) Your actual skill in using the equipment.
d) Your ability to communicate what you are doing. You could well be asked to explain why you did a certain thing, or why you used a piece of equipment in a particular way.

The tasks set will be at the level for which you are being considered. If you have moved up a level during the course, then you should have been given an opportunity of doing the practical work appropriate to this higher level.

2 INVESTI- GATIONAL WORK

You will be assessed on:

a) How you planned and prepared the set task.
b) How much relevant information you were able to obtain and use.
c) Your ability to communicate what you have done. You could be asked to talk about the investigation as well as to write a clear solution.
d) The extent to which you were able to draw a valid conclusion.
e) How far you went with the investigation. Was it exhaustive?

Very often the same investigation will be set for *all* levels. It is up to you to demonstrate how well you have been able to pursue the investigation and to decide at what point you stop.

EXAMPLE INVESTIGATION

Four straight lines all intersect each other. How many intersections will there be for other numbers of lines?

a) This work can be planned in such a way that it can become an investigation. First you can draw two lines, then three, then four, and so on.
b) You now need to look for a *pattern*. If you *can* identify a pattern you can start *predicting* how many intersections there will be for the next sets of lines without having to draw them. At the Higher Level it is vital that you are able to generalise the patterns found.

In this case you should be able to find that for n lines there are $\dfrac{n(n-1)}{2}$ intersections.

c) The work must be written up clearly. Start with an *introduction*, telling the assessor what you were trying to do. Follow this by outlining the *method* you chose to pursue your investigation. Present a *table of results*, giving an indication of what patterns you noticed.

d) Can you draw a *conclusion*? For example, can you state how you can find the number of intersections for any given number of straight lines, say 50?

e) How far have you been able to see a pattern? Can you write a *formula* for n lines, and how many intersections will this give?

In an investigation it is up to *you* to go as far as you can. But do be *clear* and *logical* in how you set about conducting the investigation. Make sure that you write up your results neatly and on the lines suggested; introduction → method → results → conclusion.

---

3 ⟩ EXTENDED WORK

Usually the task set will be defined by the school or college from some particular starting point. Then it is up to you to determine where you take it and how far you develop it.

The main points being looked for in an extended piece of work will be:

a) *The comprehension of the task.*
   Did you understand the problem and were you able to define what you were going to do?

b) *Planning.*
   Were you able to plan out the task into different set stages to enable you to complete the task?

c) *Performance of the task.*
   How well did you undertake the set task? Did you choose appropriate methods? Did you use appropriate equipment? How have you interpreted the results from that equipment?

d) *Communication.*
   This will be both written and oral. Again a well set out introduction → method → results → conclusion will be important. Have you used helpful diagrams/tables etc? In oral work, were you able to respond to unexpected queries?

EXAMPLE OF EXTENDED WORK

Square numbers 1, 4, 9 . . . can be built up in a pattern such as in Fig. 2.1,

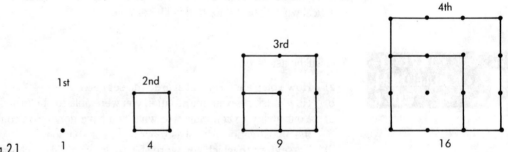

Fig. 2.1

and the nth square number is found by n^2.

Investigate patterns in triangle numbers, pentagonal numbers, etc.

Here, you could find the pattern for triangle, pentagonal and hexagonal numbers as:

■ **Triangle numbers**

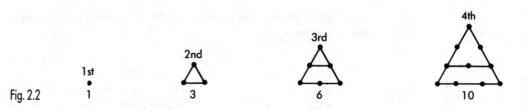

Fig. 2.2

the nth triangular number is given by $\dfrac{n(n+1)}{2}$

■ **Pentagonal numbers**

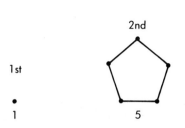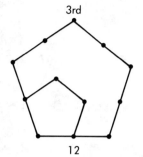

Fig. 2.3

the nth pentagonal number given by $\dfrac{n}{2}(3n-1)$

■ **Hexagonal numbers**

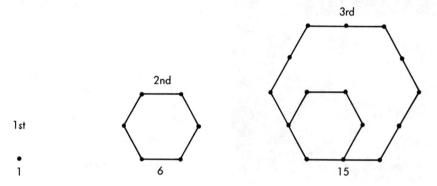

Fig. 2.4

the nth hexagonal number given by $n(2n-1)$

As you see, this task will involve some imagination and quite a bit of mathematical exploring (investigation). You will have to decide *which* numbers to include *as well as* the triangle and pentagonal numbers given. You would need to *build up* the patterns for each number type, then to look for some principle or *rule* behind the way in which each pattern is building up, and then to *generalise* that rule. Here I have only written down the results. You would, in an extended piece of work, give the method of solution, including the way in which you found the rule behind each pattern, together with any illustrations of how the rule works. You would probably also be finding the patterns for octagonal numbers and maybe more!

FINALLY

Your coursework tasks should be assessed at frequent, but appropriate, times during the course. Assessed coursework will help you to be aware of how well you are doing. If you do have shortcomings, you can then work on improving them *before* the next time such material is assessed. Yet in every case, the coursework component comes down to you, since it really does assess the way in which *you*:

■ plan the work

■ do the work

■ communicate the work.

It is all up to you!

(For more examples of coursework you can refer to the Longman Coursework book on Mathematics.)

SETS AND VENN DIAGRAMS

SET LANGUAGE AND NOTATION

USEFUL FACTS TO KNOW

SUBSETS

VENN DIAGRAMS

GETTING STARTED

You must be able to use *set notation and language*, using this to help you solve problems or to describe a solution to a problem.

The 'set' language is a powerful tool to use, and although some examination syllabuses do not examine it in itself, nevertheless they still use the language in many questions.

USEFUL DEFINITIONS

Sequence	A list of numbers that follow some pattern.
Set	A collection of elements that have something in common.
Venn diagram	A pictorial way of illustrating sets.
Union	Joined together.
Intersection	The part that is common to both.

ESSENTIAL PRINCIPLES

1 ▷ SET LANGUAGE AND NOTATION

∩ means 'intersection'; that is what is in both sets at the same time.
For example, $\{1,2,3,4,5\} \cap \{1,3,5,7,9\} = \{1,3,5\}$

∪ means 'union'; that is what is in both sets when put together.
For example, $\{7,9,10,11\} \cup \{5,7,9,11\} = \{5,7,9,10,11\}$

ℰ means 'universal set'. This defines the limit of your situation. That is, it indicates only the elements under consideration.

∅ means { } or the empty set or the 'null' set.

A′ means 'the complement of A'; that is, what is not in A.
For example, when $ℰ = \{5,6,7,8,9\}$ and $A = \{5,7,9\}$
then $A' = \{6,8\}$

n(A) means 'the number of A'; that is, how many elements are in A.
For example, if $A = \{1,3,5,7,9\}$ then $n(A) = 5$
if $B = \{a,e,i,o\}$ then $n(B) = 4$

⊂ means a 'subset of' or 'is contained in'.
For example, $\{5,7\} \subset \{1,3,5,7,9\}$

⊄ means 'not a subset of' or 'not contained in'.
For example, $\{5,7\} \not\subset \{1,2,3,4,5\}$

∈ means 'is a member of'.
For example, $8 \in \{4,8,12,16\}$

∉ means 'is not a member of'.
For example, $7 \notin \{2,4,6,8\}$

2 ▷ USEFUL FACTS TO KNOW

You can prove to yourself that the following statements are true:

1 If $A = \varnothing$ then $A' = ℰ$
If $A = ℰ$ then $A' = \varnothing$
$ℰ \cup \varnothing = ℰ$, $ℰ \cap \varnothing = \varnothing$

2 $n(A \cap B) = n(A) + n(B) - n(A \cup B)$.

This is a useful fact to learn and can be used to solve the following type of problem.

WORKED EXAMPLE 1

Of 29 people taking part in a charity cricket match one day, 16 of them had played for Yorkshire, 5 had played for Derbyshire and 11 had played for neither. How many had played for both Yorkshire and Derbyshire?

Let Y be the set of people who had played for Yorkshire,
Let D be the set of people who had played for Derbyshire.
Then from the question we can state: $n(Y) = 16$, $n(D) = 5$.
$n(Y \cup D) = 29 - 11 = 18$.
Since $n(A \cap B) = n(A) + n(D) - n(A \cup B)$
then $n(Y \cap D) = n(Y) + n(D) - n(Y \cup D)$
$= 16 + 5 - 18 = 3$.
Hence just 3 played for both Yorkshire and Derbyshire.

EXERCISE 1

If $n(A \cap C) = 8$, $n(A) = 10$, $n(A \cup C) = 15$, calculate $n(C)$.

3 ▷ SUBSETS

For a set A that has a number of n, then it will have 2^n possible different subsets.

<table>
<tr><td>

WORKED
EXAMPLE 2

</td><td>

Find all the possible subsets of the set P, where P = {2,3,5}
If we find them in the order of their number, then they are:

</td></tr>
</table>

$$\varnothing, \{2\}, \{3\}, \{5\}, \{2,3\}, \{2,5\}, \{3,5\}, \{2,3,5\}$$

We have found eight, and since $n(\text{P}) = 3$, and $2^3 = 8$, we have them all.

EXERCISE 2

Write down a possible set that has thirty two possible subsets.

4 ▷	**VENN** **DIAGRAMS**

A Venn Diagram such as Fig. 3.1 is a way of representing sets in a pictorial way. They can be useful in helping to sort out a situation, or to describe some relationship.

❝❝These can be a very
useful way to help you
think out a problem.❞❞

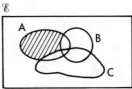

Fig. 3.1

WORKED **EXAMPLE 3**

A small sixth form was made up of only twenty three students. The following facts are known about them.

- 10 of them like bread and butter
- 7 of them are on a diet
- 8 of them who like chips but not bread and butter are not on a diet
- 5 of them like chips and bread and butter
- 6 of them like chips but are on a diet

All the dieting students who like bread and butter also like chips.
All the students either like chips or bread and butter or are on a diet.
Students who like chips and bread and butter, but who are not on a diet, will want chip sandwiches for dinner – how many will this be?

Put as much information as possible onto the Venn Diagram, as in Fig. 3.2.

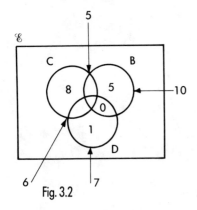

Fig. 3.2

C = students who like chips
B = students who like bread
D = students on a diet

The above information can be summarised with ease and put onto the Venn Diagram. Adding up the accounted students gives us $8 + 5 + 0 + 1 = 14$, hence we still have $23 - 14 = 9$ to account for.
i.e. $n((C \cap D) \cup (C \cap B)) = 9$, yet $n(C \cap D) = 6$ and $n(C \cap B) = 5$.
Hence $n((C \cap D) \cap (C \cap B)) = n(C \cap D) + n(C \cap B) - n((C \cap D) \cup (C \cap B))$
$$= 6 + 5 - 9 = 2$$
i.e. $n(C \cap D \cap B) = 2$

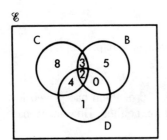

Fig. 3.3

The completed Venn Diagram will now look like Fig. 3.3; hence those who like chips and bread but are not on the diet number just 3.

Venn Diagrams can also be used to illustrate relationships, as in Fig. 3.4.

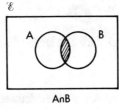

AnB

(AnB)'

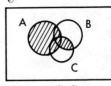

Au(BnC)

Fig. 3.4

WORKED EXAMPLE 4

Use Venn Diagrams to illustrate that (A∩B) ∪ (A∩C) = A∩ (B∪C).
If we start with (A∩B) ∪ (A∩C) as shown in Fig. 3.5, and then on another Venn Diagram we shade differently A and (B∪C), as in Fig. 3.6, the intersection is the part double shaded, which is A∩ (B∪C). By inspection we note the region A∩ (B∪C) is the same as (A∩B) ∪ (A∩C).

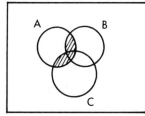

Fig. 3.5

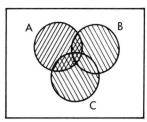

Fig. 3.6

EXERCISE 3

Show in two different ways that A∪ (B∩C) = (A∪B) ∩ (A∪C).

SOLUTION TO EXERCISES

S1
$n(A∩C) = n(A) + n(C) − n(A∪C)$
hence $8 = 10 + n(C) − 15$
hence $8 + 15 − 10 = n(C) = 13$.

S2
$32 = 2^5$, hence any set with five unique elements will do,
e.g. {a,e,i,o,u}.

S3
One way is by Venn Diagrams to show both sides are like Fig. 3.7.

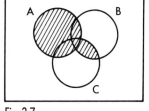

Fig. 3.7

The other way is to make up three sets A, B and C, such as
A = {2,4,6,8,10}   B = {6,8,9,10,12,14}   C = {7,8,9,10,11}
Then A∪ (B∩C) = {2,4,6,8,10} ∪ {8,9,10} = {2,4,6,8,9,10}
and (A∪B) ∩ (A∪C) = {2,4,6,8,9,10,12,14} ∩ {2,4,6,7,8,9,10,11}
                                  = {2,4,6,8,9,10}
hence A∪ (B∩C) = (A∪B) ∩ (A∪C).

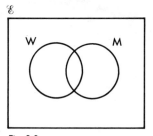

EXAM TYPE QUESTIONS

HIGHER LEVEL   **Q1**

27 children in a class are asked which TV programmes they watch. 16 watch Dr Who and 13 watch The Muppet Show. 2 do not watch either of these programmes.
a) In the Venn Diagram in Fig. 3.8,
     ℰ = {children in class}
     W = {children who watch Dr Who}
     M = {children who watch The Muppet Show}
Show in each region of the diagram, the number of children in the corresponding subset of ℰ.

Fig. 3.8

b) How many children watched only one of these programmes?   (NEA; 1988)

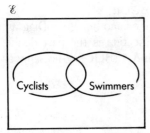

Fig. 3.9

EXTENSION

Q2

In a class of 28 pupils, there are 3 non-cyclists and 5 non-swimmers. Of the 28 pupils, 22 can both ride a cycle and swim.

a) Copy and complete the Venn Diagram using this information.

b) Find the probability that a pupil chosen at random from the class can neither swim nor ride a cycle.

(LEAG; 1988)

Q3

For a given $\mathscr{E}$, there are two subsets X and Y, such that $n(X \cup Y)' = n(X) - n(Y)$ and $n(X \cap Y) = 7$.
It is known that both $n(X)$ and $n(\mathscr{E})$ are square numbers. Find some possible solutions to $n(X)$ and $n(\mathscr{E})$.

OUTLINE ANSWERS TO EXAM QUESTIONS

A1

a) See Fig. 3.10.

b) The 12 + 9 only watched one programme, which is 21.

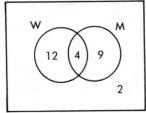

Fig. 3.10

A2

a) See Fig. 3.11.

b) $\frac{2}{28} = \frac{1}{14}$

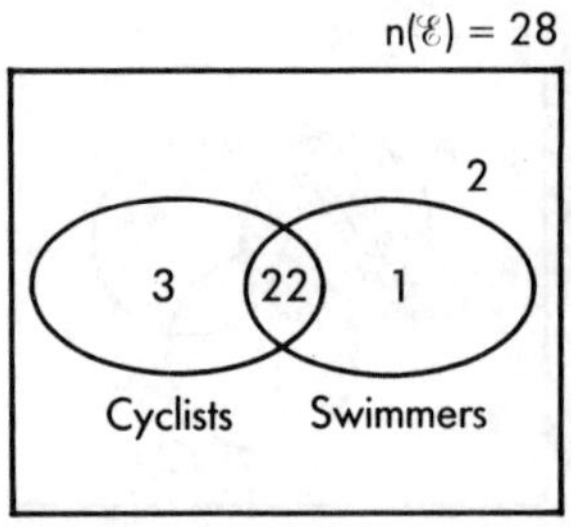

$n(\mathscr{E}) = 28$

2

3 (22) 1

Cyclists   Swimmers

Fig. 3.11

A3

Let $n(X) = x$ $n(Y) = y$,
then where $n(X) + n(Y) - n(X \cap Y) + n(X \cup Y)' = n(\mathscr{E})$.
$$x + y - 7 + (x - y) = n(\mathscr{E}).$$
$$\text{hence } 2x - 7 = n(\mathscr{E}).$$

Where $n(E)$ and x are both square numbers, then try x with
4, 9, 16, 25, 36, 49, 64, 81, 100.

$x = \quad 4 \rightarrow n(\mathscr{E}) = \quad 8 \ -7 = \quad 1$ both square but impossible for $n(\mathscr{E}) < n(X)$.
$x = \quad 9 \rightarrow n(\mathscr{E}) = \quad 18 - 7 = \quad 11$
$x = \quad 16 \rightarrow n(\mathscr{E}) = \quad 32 - 7 = \quad 25$ both square.
$x = \quad 25 \rightarrow n(\mathscr{E}) = \quad 50 - 7 = \quad 43$
$x = \quad 36 \rightarrow n(\mathscr{E}) = \quad 72 - 7 = \quad 65$
$x = \quad 49 \rightarrow n(\mathscr{E}) = \quad 98 - 7 = \quad 91$
$x = \quad 64 \rightarrow n(\mathscr{E}) = \quad 128 - 7 = \quad 121$ both square.
$x = \quad 81 \rightarrow n(\mathscr{E}) = \quad 162 - 7 = \quad 155$
$x = \quad 100 \rightarrow n(\mathscr{E}) = \quad 200 - 7 = \quad 193$

Hence the possible solutions up to $n(X) = 100$ are:
$n(X) = 16, n(\mathscr{E}) = \quad 25$
$n(X) = 64, n(\mathscr{E}) = 121.$

A STUDENT'S ANSWER WITH EXAMINER'S COMMENTS

Question

At a golf club dinner one evening, the 85 members found out that during that year all of them had either been to Spain, France or stayed in Britain for their holidays. Some of them, however, had been to more than one place. For instance, 6 of them had had a holiday in Britain and Spain but not in France, 2 of them had a holiday in Spain and France but not in Britain, and 7 of them had a holiday in all three.

The number who had a holiday in Britain only was equal to the number who had a holiday in Britain and France but not Spain. Given that 35 people had a holiday in Britain, and 25 people had a holiday in Spain, find:

a) the number who had a holiday in Britain only.
b) the number who had a holiday in Spain only.
c) the number who had a holiday in at least two different countries.
d) the number who had a holiday in France only.

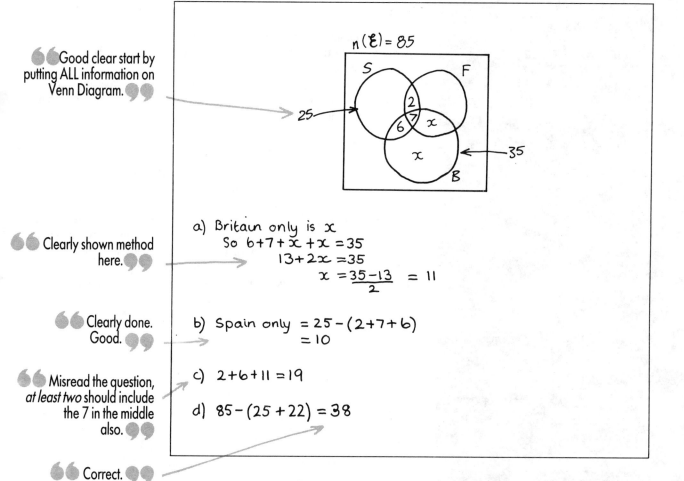

66 Good clear start by putting ALL information on Venn Diagram. **99**

66 Clearly shown method here. **99**

a) Britain only is x
   So $6 + 7 + x + x = 35$
   $13 + 2x = 35$
   $x = \dfrac{35 - 13}{2} = 11$

66 Clearly done. Good. **99**

b) Spain only $= 25 - (2 + 7 + 6)$
   $= 10$

66 Misread the question, *at least two* should include the 7 in the middle also. **99**

c) $2 + 6 + 11 = 19$

d) $85 - (25 + 22) = 38$

66 Correct. **99**

66 A well laid out answer, making just one small slip in part c). **99**

PERCENTAGE

SIMPLE PERCENTAGE

INCREASE AND DECREASE

BACKWARD PERCENTAGE

COMPOUND INTEREST

QUANTITY AS PERCENTAGE

GETTING STARTED

The application of mathematics is often examined with the use of *percentages*. In this chapter we focus on those aspects likely to be met in the examination.

Sensible *rounding off* at the appropriate time is always needed here and we show you when and how to do this so that you will not lose marks for incorrect rounding.

USEFUL DEFINITIONS

Discount	A deduction from the usual price.
Principal (amount)	Usually means the amount of money you start with in a bank account etc.
Simple Interest	Interest is paid on an *unchanged* principal amount. There is then a single formula to work out the amount of interest your money will earn.
Compound Interest	Interest is paid at regular intervals (usually each year or half year), so the principal amount *changes* from year to year.

ESSENTIAL PRINCIPLES

1 > SIMPLE PERCENTAGE

All of this chapter is devoted to percentage, and as we will be assuming the general use of a calculator, then we will always use percentage in the *decimal* form.
Eg.   1% = 0.01,   15% = 0.15,   130% = 1.30, etc.

WORKED EXAMPLE 1

Find 15% of £2.50.
15% of £2.50 is found by £2.50 × 0.15 = £0.375; we round up to give £0.38

EXERCISE 1

Which is the larger, 81% of £5.99 or 5% of £95.99?

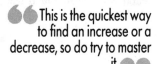

2 > INCREASE AND DECREASE

INCREASE

To increase any amount by $x\%$, use the simple routine:

change % to decimal
↓
add on 1
↓
multiply by amount.

WORKED EXAMPLE 2

Increase Gillian's wage of £126 by 6½%.
6½% = 0.065, so to find the increased wage; £126 × 1.065 = £134.19.

66 This is the quickest way to find an increase or a decrease, so do try to master it. 99

EXERCISE 2

When Sheffield Wednesday gained promotion to the first division their average attendance of 25,756 was expected to increase by about 22%. What was their new, expected, average attendance?

DECREASE

To decrease any amount by $x\%$, use a similar routine of:

change % to decimal
↓
subtract from 1
↓
multiply by amount.

WORKED EXAMPLE 3

After the Red Plague, the 526 000 population of Gallilee fell by 32%. What was the population after the Red Plague?
32% = 0.32, hence population is now 526 000 × (1 − 0.32)
    = 526 000 × 0.68 = 357 680.

EXERCISE 3

I bought a car for £900, then sold it one year later at a loss of 30%. What did I sell it for?

3 > BACKWARD PERCENTAGE

We are often told a given percentage of some amount and then need to work out the amount.
For example, the 5% of the voters who voted for M. Slater totalled 917. How many voters were there?
In this situation, we again have a simple routine which basically finds 1%, then multiplies by 100 to find the whole amount. So follow this routine:

divide given amount by %

↓

then multiply by 100.

WORKED EXAMPLE 4

The 3½ acre woodland of the Duke De Richleaux only represents 8% of his total estate. What acreage is the estate of the Duke?

Calculate $3.5 \div 8 \times 100$ to give 43.75 acres.

EXERCISE 4

When Alison Metcalf was transferred from Sheffield FC to Santos Ladies team she received £162 000 which represented 18% of the transfer fee. What was this transfer fee?

WORKED EXAMPLE 5

Mr. Cofield had a pay increase of 5% to give him a new salary of £1092 per month. What was his previous monthly salary?

The statement in effect tells us that £1092 is 105% of the previous salary, hence this is $1092 \div 105 \times 100$, which is £1040.

4 ⟩ COMPOUND INTEREST

Compound interest is the type of interest used by the commercial sector for calculating interest payments; it is a way of paying interest on your investment.

Again, it is calculated by a simple routine as illustrated in the formula:

Final amount $= P \times (1 + R)^n$

where P is the principal amount started with

R is the interest rate quoted

n is the number of times this interest is being applied.

> 66 This is like repeated simple interest year after year adding the interest onto the balance each time. 99

WORKED EXAMPLE 6

£60 is invested in an account that pays 8% compound interest each year. How much will this investment be worth in five years' time?

Since the principal amount invested is £60, the rate is 8%, and the number of times the rate is applied will be 5,

the final amount $= £60 \times (1.08)^5 = £88.159685$

$= £88.16$

Note here that it is essential that you do no rounding off *until* the final answer. You should of course have used the $\boxed{x^y}$ button on your calculator to work out the power quite quickly.

WORKED EXAMPLE 7

A new-born octopus is known to increase in body weight quite steadily at the rate of 5½% a day over the first few months of its life. What will be the weight of a baby octopus after 4 weeks if when it was born it weighed 4 kg?

The principal amount is 4 kg, the rate of increase is 5½% each day for 28 days. Hence final weight $= 4 \times (1.055)^{28}$

$= 17.9 \, \text{kg}$

> 66 This is compound interest, you need to recognise it when it is needed. 99

EXERCISE 5

When John started work he was given a starting wage of £50 a week and told it would increase by 4% every six months. How much will his weekly wage be after 5 years?

5 ⟩ QUANTITY AS PERCENTAGE

This is usually asked for as a percentage profit or loss. It is a simple extension of changing a fraction to a percentage by multiplying the fraction by 100.

WORKED EXAMPLE 8

Divinder had paid £575 for an old bike, done it up and then sold it for £750. What was his profit as a percentage of his original cost?

The profit was £750 − £575 which is £175. This as a percentage of the original cost of £575 is found by calculating $175 \div 575 \times 100$ which is 30.4% (rounded off).

EXERCISE 6

When a metal bar is heated to 300°C it expands from 41 cm to 41.3 cm. What is the expansion as a percentage of the original length?

SOLUTIONS TO EXERCISES

S1

81% of £5.99 = $0.81 \times 5.99 = 4.8519$
5% of £95.99 = $0.05 \times 95.99 = 4.7995$
hence 81% of £5.99 is larger than 5% of £95.99.

S2

$25\,756 \times (1 + 0.22) = 25\,756 \times 1.22 = 31\,422$ (rounded off).

S3

£900 $\times (1 - 0.3) = $ £900 $\times 0.7 = $ £630.

S4

£162 000 $\div 18 \times 100 = $ £900 000.

S5

Principal amount is £50, rate is 4% applied 10 times.
Hence final wage $= 50 \times (1.04)^{10} = $ £74.01 (or £74).

S6

Expansion is 0.3 cm. As a % of the original this will be $0.3 \div 41 \times 100 = 0.73\%$

HIGHER LEVEL

EXAM TYPE QUESTIONS

Q1

DISCOUNTPRINT
30% BIGGER COLOUR PRINTS
Check your bigger print size here

FILM SIZES	135	110/DISC	126
DISCOUNTPRINTS	6 × 4	5¼ × 4	4 × 4
STANDARD	5 × 3½	4½ × 3½	3½ × 3½

Fig. 4.1

a) Use the dimensions given in the table in Fig. 4.1 to see if the '30% bigger' claim is true for film size 135. Show all your working.

b)   Figure 4.2 shows the actual sizes for a standard and a discount print for size 135.

Fig. 4.2

Measure these prints and check the claim from your measurements.

c)   Comment on the results in a) and b).   (MEG; 1988)

Q2

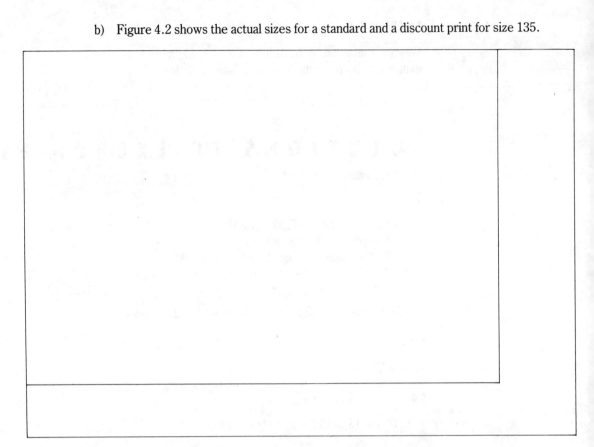

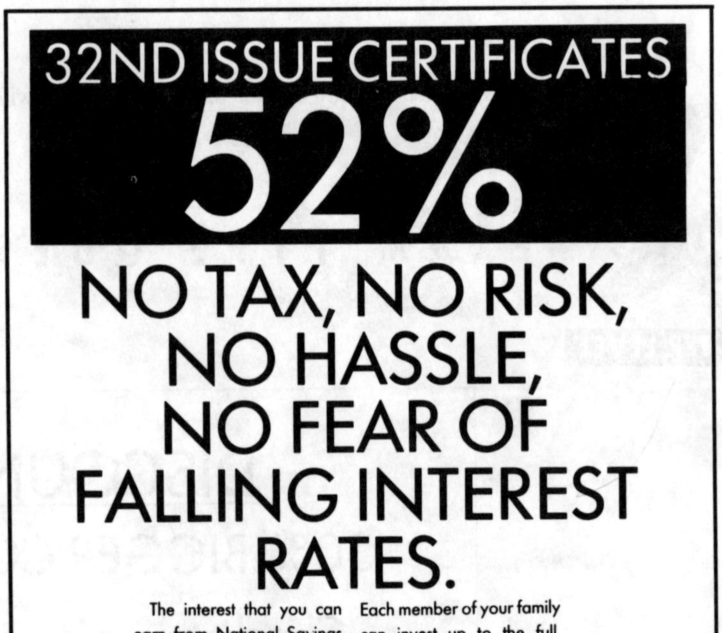

Fig. 4.3

The advertisement in Fig. 4.3 contains the following statement.
The 32nd Issue offers a guaranteed return of 52% after 5 years.
This is equivalent to 8.75% a year over the five years.

a) Investigate the truth of this statement by completing the table in Fig. 4.4 to show the year by year growth of an initial investment of £1000 at 8.75% a year.

	Amount at end of year
Year 1	
Year 2	
Year 3	
Year 4	
Year 5	

Fig. 4.4

From this table, write down, correct to one decimal place, the total percentage increase over the five years.

b) Given that National Savings Certificates are bought in multiples of £25, find the minimum amount of money which would have to be invested initially in order to produce a total of at least £1000 at the end of the five years. (NEA; 1988)

Q3

Sally put £250 into a savings account which paid interest at the rate of 8% per annum.

a) Find the amount in the account at the end of one year.
She leaves this amount of money in the account for another year. During this year the rate of interest is 9.75% per annum for the whole year.

b) Find, to the nearest penny, the amount in the account at the end of the second year.
(LEAG; 1988)

Q4

A trade union negotiates the following rise in wages on behalf of its members:

5% of weekly wage or £6 per week, whichever is the greater.

One employee finds that, for him, there is no difference between a rise of 5% and a rise of £6 per week. Calculate this employee's weekly wage before the rise. (NEA; 1988)

Q5

Supergrowth Unit Trust claims that the value of its units is likely to grow by 21% compound interest per annum. Assuming that this claim is true, calculate the value, after 5 years, of an investment of £1000 in Supergrowth Unit Trust. (MEG; 1988)

Q6

Figure 4.5 shows a floppy disc for a microcomputer. The useful area is shaded. Find the percentage of the area of the disc that is useful. (MEG; 1988)

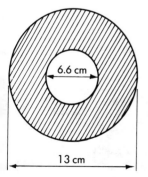

Fig. 4.5

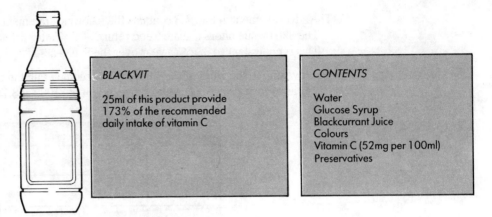

Fig. 4.6

Q7

The information in Fig. 4.6 was given on two labels taken from a bottle of 'Blackvit', a blackcurrant drink. Calculate, from the information provided, the recommended daily intake of vitamin C. (NEA; 1988)

Q8

Mr. & Mrs. Williams invest £1000 in an investment account which pays 10.5% per annum interest.

a) How much interest do they get in a year?

b) They have to pay tax on this interest at the rate of 27p in the £1. How much tax do they pay? How much of the interest is left after paying tax?

c) What percentage is this 'after tax' interest of their £1000 investment? (WJEC; 1988)

Q9

A flower is placed in a vase. During the course of each day, it loses 5% of its water content. It will begin to droop after losing 25% of its original water content.

a) What percentage of its original water content will it lose in two days?

b) If the flower had drooped after x days, what is the minimum possible value of x? (NEA; 1988)

Q10

A man invests £200 in a savings account at an annual rate of interest of 7%. He makes no further deposits or withdrawals. Interest is added each year and then itself earns extra interest (ie compound interest).

a) How much will he have in his account at the end of the second year?

b) After how many complete years will he first have more than £300 in his account? (MEG; 1988)

EXTENSION

Q11

a) A function p is defined by $p(x) = (1 + x)(1 - 0.6x)$ for the domain $0 \leqslant x \leqslant 0.5$.

   i) Complete the table in Fig. 4.7.

x	0	0.05	0.10	0.15	0.20	0.25	0.30	0.35	0.40	0.45	0.50
$1 + x$	1	1.05	1.10	1.15	1.2	1.25	1.3	1.35	1.40	1.45	1.50
$1 - 0.6x$	1	0.97	0.94	0.91	0.88	0.85	0.82	0.79	0.76	0.73	0.70
$p(x)$	1	1.019	1.034	1.047	1.056	1.063	1.066	1.067	1.064	1.058	1.050

Fig. 4.7

   ii) Draw the graph of $p(x)$ for the domain $0 \leqslant x \leqslant 0.5$.

b)   A theatre finds that when it raises its prices, the percentage increase in the price is directly proportional to the percentage decrease in the number of people attending the theatre. When the prices were increased by 10%, 6% fewer people came.

   i)   What percentage reduction in the audience will there be for a 1% rise in prices?

   ii)   What percentage change in the takings will there be for a 1% rise in prices?

   iii)   Using your graph drawn in part a), find what percentage rise in prices will give the greatest rise in takings.

c)   The theatre takes £380 per night before the rise. What is the most it can take after the rise?   (WJEC; 1988)

OUTLINE ANSWERS TO EXAM QUESTIONS

A1

a)   Standard size area $= 5 \times 3.5 = 17.5$
Discount size area $= 24$, an increase of 6.5.

The percentage increase is $\dfrac{6.5}{17.5} \times 100 = 37\%$.

Yes, the claim is true for the size 135.

b)   Standard size area $= 12.9 \times 8.8 = 113.52$
Discount size area $= 15 \times 10.2 = 153$, an increase of 39.48.

The percentage increase is $\dfrac{39.48}{113.52} \times 100 = 34.8\%$.

Yes, the claim is true for these measurements.

c)   The given sizes which are probably rounded off imperial measurements, and the metric sizes both give more than 30% increase, which is what the advertisement is saying – at least 30% bigger.

A2

a)   The table can be built up by multiplying each previous figure by 1.0875 to give the figures:

    year 1 → 1087.5
    year 2 → 1182.6563 (1182.66)
    year 3 → 1286.1387 (1286.14)
    year 4 → 1398.6758 (1398.68)
    year 5 → 1521.0599 (1521.06)
(The rounding off should only be done after all the calculations.)

The percentage increase will be $\dfrac{1521.06 - 1000}{1000} \times 100 = 52.1\%$.

Hence the statement is true.

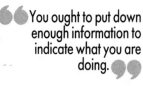
66 You ought to put down enough information to indicate what you are doing. 99

b)   If £x is invested then after 5 years it will be worth

    $x \times (1.0875)^5 = 1.52106x$
    For this investment to be at least £1000, then $1.52106x \geqslant 1000$
    hence $x \geqslant £1000 \div 1.52106$
    $x \geqslant £657.44$.
    Yet this value must be a multiple of 25, hence the value of x will be £675.

A3

a)   £250 $\times$ 1.08 = £270.

b)   £270 $\times$ 1.0975 = £296.325 = £296.33 (to nearest penny).

A4

If his wage before the rise is £x, then 5% is 0.05x, which equals £6.
Hence x = £6 ÷ 0.05 = £120.

A5

Principal amount is £1000, rate is 21%, applied 5 times, to give the final
amount = $1000 \times (1.21)^5$
        = £2593.74

A6

Inner circle = $\pi \times (3.3)^2$
Outer circle = $\pi \times (6.5)^2$
Useful area   = $\pi (6.5^2 - 3.3^2)$
So the percentage of disc that is useful is given by:

$$\frac{\pi(6.5^2 - 3.3^2)}{\pi(6.5^2)} \times 100 = 74.2\%.$$

A7

Bottle contains vitamin C at 52 mg per 100 ml, that is $\frac{52}{4}$ mg per 25 ml, which is 13 mg.

Hence 173% of recommended dose = 13 mg, so recommended dose = $\frac{13}{173} \times 100 =$
7.51 mg.

A8

a) £1000 × 0.105 = £105

b) 105 × 27p × 2835p = £28.35 tax paid.
    Interest left = £(105 − 28.35) = £76.65

c) $\frac{76.65}{1000} \times 100 = 7.665\%.$

A9

a) After the 1st day it has 0.95% of its original water content, then after 2 days it will
    have $(0.95)^2\%$ of its original water content, which is 0.9025, hence the plant has lost
    (100 − 90.25)% which is 9.75%.

b) If the flower has drooped after x days, then $(0.95)^x < 0.75$,
    By trial of $x = 1$, $x = 2$, etc. we find that $(0.95)^5 = 0.77378$
                                              and $(0.95)^6 = 0.73509$.
    So the smallest integer value of x to satisfy the situation is 6.

A10

a) £(200) × $(1.07)^2$ = £228.98.

b) $200 \times (1.07)^x \geq 300$
    $\rightarrow$ $(1.07)^x \geq 1.5$
    By trial of $x = 1, 2, 3 \ldots$ we find that $1.07^5 = 1.40$
                                              and $1.07^6 = 1.5007$.
    So after 6 complete years there will be more than £300 in the account.

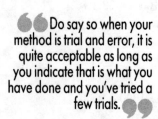
**Do say so when your
method is trial and error, it is
quite acceptable as long as
you indicate that is what you
have done and you've tried a
few trials.**

A11

a) i) The final figures to put in the table will be
            p(0.2) = 1.056   p(0.3) = 1.066   p(0.45) = 1.0585.
    ii) You should have a smooth quadratic curve like the top of a small hill.

b) % increase in price (P)∝ % decrease in audience (A).
    Hence P = KA (K being the constant of proportionality).
    When P = 10, A = 6,

hence $10 = 6K \rightarrow K = \dfrac{5}{3}$

i) When $P = 1$, $A = 1 \div \dfrac{5}{3} = \dfrac{3}{5} = 0.6\%$.

ii) (Original takings) $\times 0.994 \times 1.01 =$ (Original takings) $\times 1.00394$.
So the change in takings will be 0.394% increase.

iii) We can now see that the horizontal x axis represents the % change in prices, while the vertical $p(x)$ represents the % change in takings. The top of the hill on the graph will give us the maximum rise in takings. This is where the graph is at $x = 0.33$. So the percentage rise in prices is 33%.

c) From the graph, when $x = 0.33$, $p(x) = 1.067$, which represents the increase. So the most the theatre could take would be £380 $\times$ 1.067, which is £405.46, which should be rounded off to give a final answer of £405.

A STUDENT'S ANSWER WITH EXAMINER'S COMMENTS

Question

In January 1988, an engineering firm made 20% profit on their cost prices by selling machines for £3200. The cost of manufacturing the car was made up of wages, raw materials, electricity and maintenance in the ratios 16 : 6 : 2 : 1. During the year wages rose by 6%, the cost of raw materials rose by 15%, electricity charges rose by 12% and maintenance went up by 30%.

a) Find the manufacturer's cost price in January 1988.

b) Find the increase in the total cost of manufacturing during the year.

c) After these rises the firm decided to reduce its profit to 18% of the cost price. Find the new selling price.

d) Calculate the percentage profit at the end of the year if the selling price did not change from the beginning of the year.

Good correct method.

Not the simplest method but correct.

Not finished the question.

Correct.

Good, well laid out.

a) £3200 ≡ 120% of cost price
Cost price = $\dfrac{3200}{120} \times 100$ = £2666·67

b) 16+6+2+1 = 25
New wages = $\dfrac{16}{25} \times 2666·67 \times 1·06$ = £1809·07

raw material = $\dfrac{6}{25} \times 2666·67 \times 1·15$ = £736

electricity = $\dfrac{2}{25} \times 2666·67 \times 1·12$ = £238·93

maintenance = $\dfrac{1}{25} \times 2666·67 \times 1·30$ = £138·67

total new cost = £2922·67

c) selling price = £2922·67 $\times$ 1·18 = £3448·75

d) profit = 2922·67 − 3200 = 277·33
% profit = $\dfrac{277·33}{2922·67} \times 100$ = 9·49%

This good answer was somewhat spoilt by the simple error of not finishing the question in part b). Otherwise, the answer has been very clearly presented showing what has been done.

NUMBER

PATTERNS IN NUMBER

SEARCHING FOR PATTERN

GENERATING A SEQUENCE

GENERALISING

ITERATION

GETTING STARTED

One of the most common situations to be examined on the extension papers is number patterns and iterations. At the higher level of GCSE you are expected to be able to *generalise* a number pattern and then to use this to make *predictions*. These patterns and iterations will occur in combination with quite a few other topics also, as you will see in the exam questions.

USEFUL DEFINITIONS

Iterative   A mathematical procedure in which repetition of the same process produces results getting closer and closer to some unknown value.

ESSENTIAL PRINCIPLES

1 ▷ PATTERNS IN NUMBER

Both in coursework, and in your final end of course examination, you will be expected to investigate, work out and recognise a variety of number patterns.

Some of these will be based on the following:

Prime numbers
   2, 3, 5, 7, 11, 13, 17, 19, 23 . . .

Square numbers
   1, 4, 9, 16, 25, 36, 49, 64, 81 . . .

These two sequences must be learnt and therefore readily recognised in unfamiliar places.

WORKED EXAMPLE 1

Find the next three numbers in the sequence,

   4, 9, 25, 49, _, _, _

I first recognise that all the numbers are square numbers, and hence can re-write the series as:

   $2^2, 3^2, 5^2, 7^2$

Now recognise that it is the prime numbers being squared, so the next three will be:

   $11^2, 13^2, 17^2$, which is 121, 169, 289.

EXERCISE 1

Find the next three numbers in the sequence 1, 16, 36, 64, 81, _, _, _

2 ▷ SEARCHING FOR PATTERN

The most common way is to look at the *differences*. This will in fact help you to find most of the patterns and then to continue them.

WORKED EXAMPLE 2

Find the next three numbers in the sequence 3, 7, 11, 15, 19, _, _, _
Looking at the *differences* we see:

   $3 \rightarrow \quad 7 \rightarrow \quad 11 \rightarrow \quad 15 \rightarrow \quad 19 \rightarrow$
   $\quad +4 \quad\quad +4 \quad\quad +4 \quad\quad +4$

so the pattern can be continued by simply adding on 4 each time, to give 23, 27 and 31.

WORKED EXAMPLE 3

Find the next three numbers in the sequence 5, 6, 8, 11, 15, 20, _, _, _
Looking at the differences we see:

   $5 \rightarrow \quad 6 \rightarrow \quad 8 \rightarrow \quad 11 \rightarrow \quad 15 \rightarrow \quad 20 \rightarrow$
   $\quad +1 \quad\quad +2 \quad\quad +3 \quad\quad +4 \quad\quad +5$

so the pattern can be continued by adding on 6 then 7 then 8 to give 26, 33, 41.

EXERCISE 2

Find the next three numbers in each of the following sequences:
   i) 4, 6, 9, 14, 21, 32, _, _, _
   ii) 100, 95, 90, 85, _, _, _
   iii) 10, 11, 15, 24, 40, _, _, _

It is vital that you look at the differences in a number sequence to help you find the pattern. However, sometimes you will need to consider the 'second differences' to continue the pattern.

WORKED EXAMPLE 4

Find the next three numbers in the sequence 2, 3, 7, 17, 36, _, _, _
Looking at the differences we see:

$$2 \;\to\; 3 \;\to\; 7 \;\to\; 17 \;\to\; 36$$
$$+1 \;\to\; +4 \;\to\; +10 \;\to\; +19$$
$$+3 \qquad +6 \qquad +9$$

It is now in the 'second differences' that we notice a pattern and can continue it to give:

$$36 \;\to\; 67 \;\to\; 113 \;\to\; 177$$
$$+19 \;\to\; +31 \;\to\; +46 \;\to\; +64$$
$$+9 \qquad +12 \qquad +15 \qquad +18$$

hence the next three numbers are 67, 113 and 177.

EXERCISE 3

Find the next three numbers in the sequence 1, 3, 6, 11, 20, 37, _, _, _

This technique of looking for differences can, if required, be continued on to the 'third differences', or even further. When answering this type of question you should always illustrate *how* you found your pattern.

These patterns will very often be part of a longer investigation type question where you would probably also be asked for the general term or the nth term, which we consider later in this chapter.

3 ▷ GENERATING A SEQUENCE

At times you will be given a rule to follow so as to generate a number pattern.

WORKED EXAMPLE 5

U_n is the nth term in a sequence. If $U_n = \dfrac{n(n+1)}{2}$ then generate the first five terms of this sequence and describe the type of numbers generated.

The first five terms are found by substituting into the formula $U_n = \dfrac{n(n+1)}{2}$ the numbers $n = 1, 2, 3, 4, 5$ to give

$$\frac{1 \times 2}{2}, \; \frac{2 \times 3}{2}, \; \frac{3 \times 4}{2}, \; \frac{4 \times 5}{2}, \; \frac{5 \times 6}{2},$$
$$= 1 \;, \quad 3 \;, \quad 6 \;, \quad 10 \;, \quad 15 \;,$$

This pattern is the 'triangle numbers' usually found by considering *triangular patterns* as in Fig. 5.1

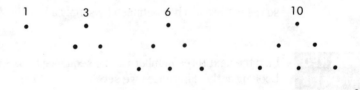

Fig. 5.1

EXERCISE 4

Generate the first few terms of the sequence given by: $U_n = n(2n - 1)$.

Alternative Notation

This can also be done by defining how the terms use the *one before* to build upon. For example, the nth term of a sequence could be given by the formula

$$U_n = 3 + 2.U_{(n-1)}$$

So where

$U_1 = 5$ then we would calculate the following terms as:
$U_2 = 3 + 2 \times 5 = 13$
$U_3 = 3 + 2 \times 13 = 29$
$U_4 = 3 + 2 \times 29 = 61$ etc.

This process is more commonly used in *iterations* which come later in the chapter.

4 ⟩ GENERALISING

This is where, from a given pattern of numbers, you try to state the pattern *algebraically*, as in the section above. This can be a long investigation by trial and error, but if you can learn some simple patterns to recognise, and some simple rules to follow, then you will find the generalisations more quickly.

Rules to follow

a) Look first to see if it is an obvious pattern or one you've remembered.

b) Look at the *differences* to see what type of relationship you are looking for. If the *first* differences do not reveal anything, try the *second* or *third* differences, and so on.

c) Break the sequences up into *factors* to see what other links you can find.

We now look in more detail at these procedures.

a) COMMON PATTERNS

i) 2, 4, 6, 8, 10 .... $2n$

ii) 2, 4, 8, 16 .... 2^n

iii) 1, 4, 9, 16, 25 .... n^2

iv) 1, 3, 6, 10, 15 .... $\dfrac{n(n+1)}{2}$

iv) are the triangle numbers, well worth recognising when you see it.

b) LOOKING AT DIFFERENCES

Same difference

If between each term you find the same difference, d, then where 'a' is the first number in the sequence, the nth term will be given by

$$U_n = a + d(n - 1)$$

WORKED EXAMPLE 6

Find the nth term in the sequence 4, 7, 10, 13, 16 . . .
We notice that the difference is always 3, and the first term is 4, hence the nth term will be $4 + 3(n - 1)$, which could be simplified to $3n + 1$.

EXERCISE 5

Find the nth term in the following sequence 7, 12, 17, 22 . . .

Multiple differences

If the differences give recognisable multiples of, say, m, then where the first term is 'a' the nth term will be given by

$$U_n = a + m \frac{n(n-1)}{2}$$

WORKED EXAMPLE 7

Find the nth term in the sequence 1, 4, 10, 19, 31 . . .
We notice that the differences are 3, 6, 9, 12, the multiples of 3, and that the first term is 1, hence the nth term will be given by

$$U_n = 1 + 3 \frac{n(n-1)}{2}$$

EXERCISE 6

Find the nth term of the sequence 8, 15, 29, 50, 78 . . .

Square differences

If the differences give the square numbers, ie 1, 4, 9, 16, 25 . . . then where the first term is 'a', the nth term will be given by

$$a + \frac{n}{6}(n+1)(2n+1)$$

WORKED EXAMPLE 8

Find the nth term of the sequences 6, 7, 11, 20, 36 . . .
We notice that the differences are 1, 4, 9, 16, . . ., and that the first term is 6, hence the nth term is given by

$$U_n = 6 + \frac{n}{6}(n+1)(2n+1)$$

Triangle differences

If the differences give the well known triangle numbers, ie 1, 3, 6, 10, 15, . . ., and a first term of a, then the nth term will be given by

$$U_n = a + \frac{n}{6}(n+1)(n+2)$$

There are lots of different differences that can now link to one of the above types, and hence you can generalise the sequence. However, do look carefully at the differences as they may be a multiple or a factor of one of the above types.

WORKED EXAMPLE 9

Find the nth term of the sequence 8, 10, 16, 28, 48, . . .
We notice the differences are 2, 6, 12, 20 . . . which are not recognisable until you halve them to get 1, 3, 6, 10 . . . (the triangle numbers). Hence the nth term will be given by

$$U_n = 8 + 2 \times \frac{n}{6}(n+1)(n+2)$$

$$U_n = 8 + \frac{n}{3}(n+1)(n+2)$$

EXERCISE 7

Find the nth term of the sequence 1, 9, 25, 49 . . .

c) FIND FACTORS

Sometimes we look at the differences and see nothing, we go to second differences and see nothing. If this is the case then we can look at *factors* of the sequence and see how they are being built up. For example, look at the triangle numbers:

1, 3, 6, 10, 15, 21 . . .

Looking at the differences gives us 2, 3, 4, 5, . . ., but how does this help us to find U_n? Well actually it can do, but that would be taking us into much higher mathematics. Suppose instead that we write down the *factors* of each term; we then have:

$$
\begin{array}{cccccc}
1 & 3 & 6 & 10 & 15 & 21 \\
\downarrow & \downarrow & \downarrow & \downarrow & \downarrow & \downarrow \\
1\times1 & 1\times3 & 2\times3 & 2\times5 & 3\times5 & 3\times7
\end{array}
$$

There seems nothing to see first of all; but then on closer inspection we see that if we *double* the *smaller of each factor* we get the interesting pattern:

$$
\begin{array}{cccccc}
1 & 3 & 6 & 10 & 15 & 21 \\
\downarrow & \downarrow & \downarrow & \downarrow & \downarrow & \downarrow \\
1\times1 & 1\times3 & 2\times3 & 2\times5 & 3\times5 & 3\times7
\end{array}
$$

double 1 term:

$$
\begin{array}{cccccc}
(1\times2) & (2\times3) & (4\times3) & (4\times5) & (6\times5) & (6\times7) \\
\downarrow & \downarrow & \downarrow & \downarrow & \downarrow & \downarrow \\
\tfrac{1}{2}(1\times2) & \tfrac{1}{2}(2\times3) & \tfrac{1}{2}(3\times4) & \tfrac{1}{2}(4\times5) & \tfrac{1}{2}(5\times6) & \tfrac{1}{2}(6\times7) \\
\downarrow & \downarrow & \downarrow & \downarrow & \downarrow & \downarrow \\
U_1 & U_2 & U_3 & U_4 & U_5 & U_6
\end{array}
$$

which gives us very neatly

$$U_n \rightarrow \tfrac{1}{2}n(n+1).$$

So, when looking for patterns:

a) look for *familiar* patterns you've seen before
b) look at the *differences*
c) look at the *factors*.

EXERCISE 8

Find the nth term of the sequence 3, 8, 15, 24 . . .

5 > ITERATION

An *iteration* is when a *generating term*, U_n, is used to *keep generating terms* until a certain situation is satisfied.

Example – A solution to the equation $x^2 - 2x - 3 = 0$ can be found by re-writing the equation in the form: $x^2 = 3 + 2x$

Dividing by x gives $x = \dfrac{3}{x} + 2$

Suppose we assume a *starting solution* x_1 to this equation as being $x_1 = 2$. We now find the value this 'starting solution' makes the right hand side of the equation. We find that

$$x_2 = \frac{3}{x_1} + 2 = \frac{3}{2} + 2 = 3.5$$

We then use this value of $x_2 = 3.5$ as a *better solution* in the equation. We now get

$$x_3 = \frac{3}{3.5} + 2 = 2.857 \text{ (the rest is in the calculator).}$$

> **This is ideal to work through on a computer, have a go and just see how accurate it can be.**

By *continuing* this process we find:

$x_4 = 3.05$
$x_5 = 2.98$
$x_6 = 3.01$
$x_7 = 3.00$
$x_8 = 3.00$

The process was continued until the value to 2 decimal places was the same two times. The actual calculator value was used each time in the iteration. Hence the solution here is $x = 3$, which can be shown to be correct.

WORKED EXAMPLE 10

Show that an iteration formula to solve the equation

$$x^3 - 5x + 1 = 0 \text{ is } x_{n+1} = \frac{x_n{}^3 + 1}{5}.$$

Starting with $x_1 = 0$, continue the iteration until you get a solution correct to 3 decimal places.

The equation $x^3 - 5x + 1 = 0$ can be re-written to give

$$5x = x^3 + 1$$
$$\text{hence} \quad x = \frac{x^3 + 1}{5}$$

This can be solved using the iteration method where $x_{n+1} = \dfrac{(x_n)^3 + 1}{5}$

Working the iteration out to four decimal places (but keeping the accurate figure in the calculator)

$x_1 = 0$
$x_2 = (0+1)/5 = 0.2$
$x_3 = (0.2^3+1)/5 = 0.2016$
$x_4 = \qquad\qquad 0.2016.$

Hence a solution to the equation is $x = 0.2016$.

EXERCISE 9

Solve the equation, *to 3 decimal places,* $x^2 + 3x - 1 = 0$ by the iteration formula $U_{n+1} = \dfrac{1-(U_n)^2}{3}$ (starting with $U_1 = 0$), and show it as a solution.

SOLUTIONS TO EXERCISES

S1

The sequence can be rewritten as 1^2, 4^2, 6^2, 8^2, 9^2, this is the squares of the non-prime integers, hence the next three numbers are 10^2, 12^2 and 14^2 which is 100, 144 and 196.

S2

    i) Differences are the prime numbers, hence the next three numbers are 45, 62 and 81.
    ii) Differences are -5 in each case, hence the next three numbers are 80, 75 and 70.
    iii) Differences are the square numbers, hence the next three numbers are 65, 101 and 150.

S3

Look at second differences, these are 1, 2, 4, 8, (16, 32, 64) used to build down to give the next three numbers as 70, 135 and 264.

S4

$U_1 = 1$, $U_2 = 6$, $U_3 = 15$, $U_4 = 28$.

S5

The difference is always 5, and the first term is 7, hence the nth term is given by $7 + 5(n - 1)$ which could be simplified to $5n + 2$.

S6

The differences are 7, 14, 21, 28 which are the multiples of 7. The first term is 8, hence the nth term is $8 + 7\dfrac{n(n-1)}{2}$.

S7

These are 1^2, 3^2, 5^2, 7^2, the odd numbers squared. Hence we need to link up

    1st term $\rightarrow 1^2$
    2nd term $\rightarrow 3^2$
    3rd term $\rightarrow 5^2$
    4th term $\rightarrow 7^2$

hence the nth term $\rightarrow (2n - 1)^2$

S8

The differences helped me to predict the next few terms but not the nth term so readily. However, on looking at the factors I noticed:

U_1	U_2	U_3	U_4		U_n
$\downarrow$	$\downarrow$	$\downarrow$	$\downarrow$		$\downarrow$
3	8	15	24		
1×3	2×4	3×5	4×6		$n\times(n+2)$

hence $U_n = n(n+2)$.

S9

The iteration to three decimal places is:

$U_2 = 0.333$
$U_3 = 0.296$
$U_4 = 0.304$
$U_5 = 0.302$
$U_6 = 0.303$
$U_7 = 0.303$

so the solution is $x = 0.303$.

By substituting $x = 0.303$ into $x^2 + 3x + 1$ we get 0.0009, showing it to be very close to zero.

EXAM TYPE QUESTIONS

HIGHER LEVEL

Q1

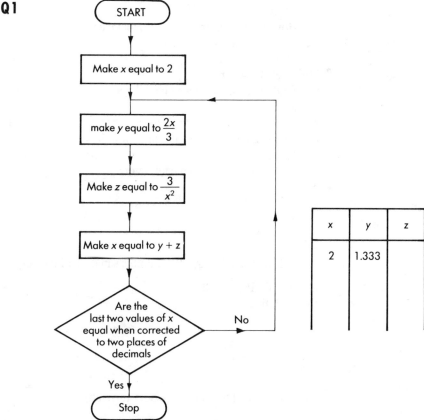

Fig. 5.2

a) Work through the flow diagram writing down the value of x, y and z in a table, as shown in Fig. 5.2, recording only the first three decimal places of your answers.

> Try to make your comment on some mathematical insight you can notice.

b) Cube the last value of x and comment on the result.
c) Give the last value of x correct to two decimal places. (MEG; 1988)

Q2

The nth term of a sequence is given by the formula

$$U_n = \frac{1}{1 + U_{n-1}} \text{ and } U_4 = 3$$

a) Calculate the value of U_5.
b) Calculate the value of U_3. (NEA; 1988)

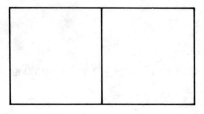

Q3

Four rods are used to make a square, as shown in Fig. 5.3.

Rods are then added to make a row of 2 squares, then 3 squares, and so on, as in Fig. 5.4.

Fig. 5.3

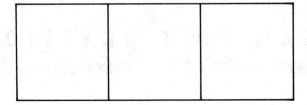

Fig. 5.4

a) How many rods are needed to make a row of
   i) 5 squares
   ii) 6 squares
   iii) 15 squares
b) Find the formula which gives the number of rods, r, needed to make a row of s squares in the form: $r =$
c) Use your formula to find how many squares could be made with 70 rods.
d) Re-arranged your formula in b) into the form: $s =$
e) What is the greatest number of squares you can make in a row with 120 rods? How many rods will you have left over?   (WJEC; 1988)

Q4

Write down the missing TWO numbers in each of the sequences:

a) 64, 32, 16, _, _, 2
b) 1, 2, 6, _, _, 720   (LEAG; 1988)

Q5

In a sequence of fractions, the next term after $\dfrac{x}{y}$ is $\dfrac{x + y}{2x + y}$.

The first term is $\dfrac{2}{3}$.

a) Write down the first six terms of the sequence $\dfrac{2}{3}, \dfrac{5}{7}, -, -, -, -, -, -$

b) Find the *squares* of the values of these six terms to as many decimal places as your calculator will give. What do you notice about these squares of values?

c) Find the term in the sequence which comes immediately before $\dfrac{2378}{3363}$

d) One term in the sequence is $\dfrac{p}{q}$. Find, in terms of p and q, the term which comes immediately before $\dfrac{p}{q}$.   (MEG; 1988)

Q6

A computer has been programmed to generate a sequence of numbers. The first six numbers that it produces are:

9, 16, 23, 30, 37, 44.

a) Write down the next two numbers of the sequence that will appear.
b) Work out the 60th number to appear.
c) Write down an expression for the rth term of the sequence.
d) How many terms of the sequence will the computer have produced when the first number over 2000 appears?   (NEA; 1988)

Q7

Figure 5.5 shows part of the graph of $f : x \rightarrow x^3 - 2x - 1$ and the solution $x = w$ of the equation $x^3 - 2x - 1 = 0$.

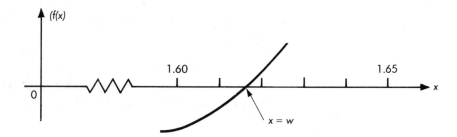

Fig. 5.5

a) From this diagram, estimate the value of w correct to two decimal places.

b) Show that $x^3 - 2x - 1 = 0$ may be written as $x = \sqrt{\left(2 + \dfrac{1}{x}\right)}$

c) Using $x_{n+1} = \sqrt{\left(2 + \dfrac{1}{x_n}\right)}$ and taking x_1 to be the value you obtained as your

estimate for w in part a), calculate x_2, x_3 and x_4. In each case, write down all the digits shown on your calculator.
d) Continue this iteration until you can give the value of w correct to five decimal places. Write down this value of w.   (LEAG; 1988)

EXTENSION

Q8

a) Here is a sequence of numbers 2, 4, 8, 16, 32, 64.
    i) Write down a formula for the nth number in this sequence.
       You can get from any number of this sequence to the next number by adding on as in Fig.5.6.

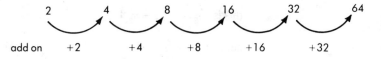

Fig. 5.6   add on   +2   +4   +8   +16   +32

    ii) The 'add on' numbers also form a sequence. What do you notice about this sequence?
    iii) Use algebra to explain why this happens.
b) Now write down this sequence 3, 9, 27, 81, 243, 729.
    i) Write down the 'add on' numbers for this sequence.
    ii) What is the connection between the 'add on' sequence and the original sequence?
    iii) Use algebra to explain why this happens.

c) If instead of starting with 2 or 3, the original sequence starts: a, a^2, a^3, a^4, what is the connection between the 'add on' sequence and the original sequence?

d) Here is an 'add on' sequence: $+20, +100, +500, +2500$.
   i) If the original sequence is of the type described in c)) write down the first five numbers of the original sequence.
   ii) Write down the first five numbers of a different original sequence (not of the type described in c)) which has the same 'add on' sequence.
   iii) Write down a formula for the nth number in the sequence you have given in ii).

(O and C; 1988)

Q9

a) The symbol $n!$ (usually called "factorial n") is used to stand for the result of multiplying together the first n whole numbers; so that, for example

$$10! = 1 \times 2 \times 3 \times 4 \times 5 \times 6 \times 7 \times 8 \times 9 \times 10$$

My calculator gives the value of 10! to be 3628800. Explain how you could tell, without actually doing the multiplication, that the value of 10! ends in just two zeros.

b) The value of 100! is too large to be found on the calculator. Find, without using your calculator, how many zeros there are at the end of 100! Explain your reasoning clearly.

c) A book of tables states that 100! is approximately 9.33×10^{157}. Putting this together with b), we know how many digits there are in 100!, that some are certainly zero and that some are certainly not zero. Making the assumption that each of the digits 0, 1, 2, ... 9 occurs about the same number of times amongst the remaining digits, estimate how many zeros there are altogether in 100! when it is written out in full. Show your working.

(O and C; 1987)

OUTLINE ANSWERS TO EXAM QUESTIONS

A1

a)
x	y	z
2	1.333	0.75
2.083	1.388	0.691
2.080		

b) Using the correct calculator value of x I get 9.0000658, and cubing 2.08 I get 8.9989, both of which round off to 9. So it would appear that this iteration has found the cube root of 9 to 2 decimal places.

c) 2.08.

A2

a) $U_5 = \dfrac{1}{1 + U_4} = \dfrac{1}{1 + 3} = 0.25.$

b) We need to re-arrange the formula to make $U_{(n-1)}$ the subject,

this is $U_{(n-1)} = \dfrac{1}{U_n} - 1$

hence $U_3 = \dfrac{1}{U_4} - 1 = \dfrac{1}{3} - 1 = -\dfrac{2}{3}.$

A3

a) Build up a table of results to give

number of squares	(s)	1	2	3	4	5	6
rods	(r)	4	7	10	13	16	19

The difference is 3 each time so the table can easily be continued, and with a difference of 3 each time and a start of 4 then the number of rods $(r) = 4 + 3(s - 1) = 4 + 3s - 3 = 1 + 3s.$

Hence   i) $r = 16$ ii) $r = 19$ iii) $r = 46$.

b)   The formula is $r = 1 + 3s$.

c)   When $r = 70$, solve the equation $70 = 1 + 3s$ to give $s = 23$.

d)   Re-arrange to give $s = \dfrac{r - 1}{3}$.

e)   When $r = 120$, $s = \dfrac{119}{3} = 39.6$.

So there will be 39 squares with 2 rods left over.

A4

a)   8, 4

b)   The differences will not help here, but looking at the factors will, since

$$1 \rightarrow 1$$
$$2 \rightarrow 1 \times 2$$
$$6 \rightarrow 1 \times 2 \times 3$$
$$?$$
$$?$$
$$720 \rightarrow 1 \times 2 \times 3 \times 4 \times 5 \times 6.$$

So the missing numbers are $(1 \times 2 \times 3 \times 4) = 24$ and $(1 \times 2 \times 3 \times 4 \times 5) = 120$.

A5

a) $\dfrac{2}{3}$, $\dfrac{5}{7}$, $\dfrac{12}{17}$, $\dfrac{29}{41}$, $\dfrac{70}{99}$, $\dfrac{169}{239}$

b)   0.4444444

0.510204

0.4982699

0.5002974

0.4999489

0.5000087

You should notice that these squares are getting closer to 0.5.

c)   You will get a pair of simultaneous equations, $x + y = 2378$

$$2x + y = 3363$$

which will solve to give $x = 985, y = 1393$. So the term is $\dfrac{985}{1393}$.

d)   Solve the pair of simultaneous equations: $x + y = p$

$$2x + y = q$$

to give $x = q - p$ and $y = 2p - q$. So the term is $\dfrac{q - p}{2p - q}$.

A6

a)   Looking at the differences, we note they are 7 each time. So the next two numbers are 51 and 58.

b)   Since the difference is 7 and the first term is 9, then the nth term is $9 + 7(n - 1)$. So the 60th term is $9 + 7 \times 59 = 422$.

c) rth term $= 9 + 7(r - 1) = 9 + 7r - 7$

$$= 7r + 2.$$

d)   When rth term > 2000 then $7r + 2 > 2000$

$$\text{hence} 7r > 1998$$
$$r > 285.4.$$

So after 286 terms the first number over 2000 appears.

A7

a)   1.62.

b) $x^3 - 2x - 1 = 0$, divide through by x gives

$$x^2 - 2 - \frac{1}{x} = 0,$$

hence $x^2 = 2 + \dfrac{1}{x}$

hence $x^2 = \sqrt{\left(2 + \dfrac{1}{x}\right)}$

c) $x_1 = 1.62$
    $x_2 = 1.6178022$
    $x_3 = 1.6180614$
    $x_4 = 1.6180308$

d) $x_5 = 1.6180344$; this now gives us the solution to 5 decimal places as $w = 1.61803$.

A8

a) i) 2^n.
    ii) It is the same sequence as the original.
    iii) Consider three consecutive terms in the original sequence $2^x, 2^{x+1}, 2^{x+2}$.
          The 'add ons' will be $2^{x+1} - 2^x$ and $2^{x+2} - 2^{x+1}$
                    which are $2^x(2 - 1)$ and $2^{x+1}(2 - 1)$
                        which is 2^x and 2^{x+1}.
          So we see the pattern as in Fig. 5.7.

Fig. 5.7

b) i) The 'add ons' are 6, 18, 54, 162, 486.
    ii) The 'add on' sequence is exactly double the original.
    iii) Consider three consecutive terms of the original sequence $3^x, 3^{x+1}, 3^{x+2}$.
          The 'add ons' will be $3^{x+1} - 3^x$ and $3^{x+2} - 3^{x+1}$
                    which are $3^x(3 - 1)$ and $3^{x+1}(3 - 1)$
                        which is 2×3^x and $2 \times 3^{x+1}$.
          So we see the pattern as in Fig. 5.8.

Fig. 5.8

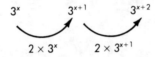

c) The 'add on' sequence will be the original sequence multiplied by $(a - 1)$.

d) i) Then from c) $a(a - 1) = 20$
          hence $a^2 - a - 20 = 0$
          which is the quadratic having solution $a = 5$ and $a = -4$. The only sensible solution is $a = 5$ which gives the sequence 5, 25, 125, 625, 3125.
    ii) 1, 21, 121, 621, 3121 . . .
    iii) The sequence 1, 21, 121, 621, 3121 . . . U_n
          Add 4 on to each term will give 5, 25, 125, 625, 3125 . . . $U_n + 4$
          The nth term of this sequence is 5^n; hence $U_n + 4 = 5^n$, so the nth term will be $5^n - 4$.

A9

a) Pairs of numbers that multiply to give a multiple of 10 can be found to be (2×5), and then 10 itself, will each give a zero on the end. None of the other numbers can multiply together to give any zeros. So just (2×5) and 10 contribute a zero, hence two zeros.

b) Finding pairs that give multiples of 10, and the multiples of 10 give us
    $(2 \times 5), (4 \times 15), (6 \times 25), (8 \times 35), (12 \times 45)$ . . . (24×95) [10 of them]
    and $\times 10 \times 20 \times 30 \times 40 \times 50 \times 60 \times 70 \times 80 \times 90 \times 100$ [another 10 of them]
    gives 20 zeros altogether. (Note you can only use any number once.)

c) There will be $157 + 1$ digits altogether, 20 of which are known to be zero, this leaves 138 left. There is a $\frac{1}{10}$ probability of any other digits being a zero, hence I would expect to find one tenth of 138, which is approximately 14, other zeros. So $14 + 20 = 34$ zeros altogether.

A STUDENT'S ANSWER
WITH EXAMINER'S COMMENTS

Question

A black ball is placed on a table and is represented by T_1, as shown in the diagram.

It is then surrounded by white balls to form a triangular shape, T_2, as shown in the diagram.

Shape T_3 is formed by surrounding T_2 by black balls, and so on.

T_1

a) What kind of triangles are formed by the centres of the outside balls?

   isosolese

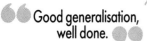
Spelling incorrect, but as long as the word is recognisable then no marks will be lost.

b) How many rows of balls will there be in

   i) shape T_7? 1, 3, 5, 6, 7, 9, 11, 13

   ii) shape T_n?

   $2n - 1$

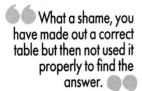
You have ended up in the right place, but have not specifically given the answer.

T_2

T_3

c) How many balls will there be in

   i) shape T_7? 1, 9, 25, 49, 81, 121, 169

   ii) shape T_n? $(2n-1)^2$

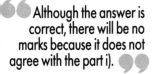
Good generalisation, well done.

What a shame, you have made out a correct table but then not used it properly to find the answer.

d) What colour balls will be added

   i) to T_{17} to make T_{18}?

   black

   ii) To T_{2n-1} to make T_{2n}?

   white

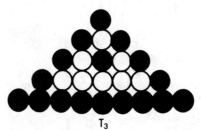

Black	White
T_1	T_2
T_3	T_4
T_5	T_6
T_7	T_8
odd	even

Although the answer is correct, there will be no marks because it does not agree with the part i).

e) How many balls will be added to T_{n-1} to make T_n?

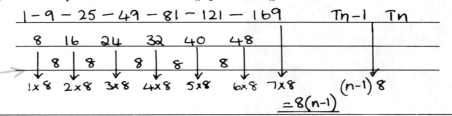

1 — 9 — 25 — 49 — 81 — 121 — 169 T_{n-1} T_n

   8   16   24   32   40   48

   8   8   8   8   8

1×8 2×8 3×8 4×8 5×8 6×8 7×8 $(n-1)8$

$= 8(n-1)$

Very good, clearly showing how the final answer is found.

A good answer showing high mathematical ability but a tendency to make careless errors which will be costly.

RATIO AND VARIANCE

SIMILAR SHAPES

VARIATION

GETTING STARTED

We consider here the ratios of similar shapes and the three different types of variance, all of which appear in the majority of GCSE mathematics syllabuses and on the extension papers.

This section will incorporate quite a bit of algebra also.

USEFUL DEFINITIONS

Similar	Two shapes are similar if one is a mathematical enlargement of the other.
Enlargement	When all the respective dimensions of two shapes are in the same ratio.
Scale factor	The ratio which links two similar figures.
Variation	Where one or more variables are connected by an algebraic rule.
Proportional	Having a constant ratio.
Surd	An expression left in 'root' notation, e.g. $\sqrt{2}$, $\sqrt{15}$.

ESSENTIAL PRINCIPLES

1 **SIMILAR SHAPES**

Two shapes are said to be *similar* if all their corresponding angles are equal and the ratios of the corresponding lengths are also equal. An example is shown in Fig. 6.1.

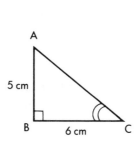
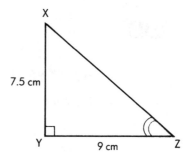

Fig. 6.1

All the corresponding angles are equal and the ratio of each pair of corresponding sides is 2:3

i.e. $\dfrac{5}{7.5} = \dfrac{6}{9} = \dfrac{2}{3}$

So if the length AC is 7.8 cm, then the length XZ can be found by equating $\dfrac{XZ}{7.8} = \dfrac{3}{2}$

hence $XZ = \dfrac{3 \times 7.8}{2} = 11.7$ cm. (Note how the ratio has been used.)

RATIOS OF SIMILAR SHAPES

Consider the two shapes shown in Fig. 6.2.

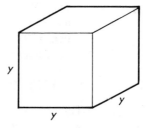

Fig. 6.2

Both these shapes are *cubes*; hence each *corresponding angle* is the same, and each *corresponding side* is in the ratio $x{:}y$. We can now also see that by considering any *face*, the ratio of the *areas* is $x^2 : y^2$. The ratio of the *volumes* is $x^3 : y^3$.

We can summarise the situation by saying that for any similar solid that has lengths in the ratio $x{:}y$ then:

> These ratio's are asked about every year you must learn them.

- ratio of lengths $x{:}y$
- ratio of areas $x^2{:}y^2$
- ratio of volume $x^3{:}y^3$

WORKED EXAMPLE 1

A 500 g box of Brekko has the dimensions 8 cm by 20 cm by 30 cm. The firm wanted to pack a similar box with 350 g of Brekko. What would be the dimensions of this new box?

The ratio of the volumes of the box will be in the ratio of 500 : 350. This ratio can be simplified to $\dfrac{500}{500} : \dfrac{350}{500}$ which is 1 : 0.7. Hence if the ratio of the volume is 1 : 0.7 the ratio of the lengths will be $\sqrt[3]{1} : \sqrt[3]{0.7} = 1 : 0.8879$.

So each side of the larger box will be reduced by a factor of 0.8879, hence the new dimensions are found by:

8 cm × 0.8879, 20 cm × 0.8879, 30 cm × 0.8879
which will be: 7.1 cm, 17.8 cm, 26.6 cm.

EXERCISE 1

Two similar tins of soup have similar labels on them of areas 15 cm^2 and 20 cm^2 respectively. If the smaller tin contains 400 g of soup, how much will the larger tin hold?

2 ⟩   VARIATION

There are three types of *variation*, or *proportion*, that we need to consider – direct, inverse and joint.

DIRECT PROPORTION

Direct proportion is when there is a simple multiplying factor between two things, so as one increases so does the other. For example, the amount of paint needed to paint a wall is *directly proportional* to the area of the wall. The bigger the wall, the more paint will be needed.

The variation can be, and often is, related to the *square* or the *cube* of something. For example, the volume of a sphere varies directly with the cube of the radius. The alternative ways of saying "varies directly with" include the following:

❝❝ The exam questions will often use words like these. ❞❞

- the amount of paint *varies directly with* the area of the wall
- the amount of paint *is directly proportional to* the area of the wall
- the amount of paint ∝ the area of the wall
- the amount of paint = K × (the area of the wall).

The last two are mathematically the most convenient and we will use this shorthand a lot. The K is a constant value called the *constant of proportionality*.

WORKED EXAMPLE 2

The mass of a sphere varies directly with the cube of the radius. A sphere with radius 5 cm has a mass of 523.6 g.
Find the mass of a similar sphere with radius 8 cm.

Since V ∝ r^3 then V = Kr^3,
and then V = 523.6g when r = 5 cm
hence 523.6 = 125K, or K = 4.1888.
So when r = 8,   V = 4.1888 × 8^3 = 2144.7 g

EXERCISE 2

The square of the orbital period, P days, of a planet varies directly with the cube of its mean distance, d km, from the sun. The earth has an orbital period of 365.25 days, and has a mean distance of 149.7 million kilometres from the sun.
Calculate the orbital period of Mercury, the closest planet to the sun, with a mean distance of 58 million kilometres from the sun.

INVERSE PROPORTION

Inverse proportion is when there is a dividing connection between two things, so that as one increases the other decreases. For example, as as I drive home and decide to increase the *speed*, then the *time taken* for the journey decreases. So speed and time taken are inversely proportional.

WORKED EXAMPLE 3

The time taken to dig a field of potatoes varies inversely with the square root of the number of people digging. If it takes 8 men 6 hours to dig out a field of potatoes, then how long will it take 10 men?

Since time (t) ∝ $\dfrac{1}{\sqrt{(\text{number of men } (n))}}$

then $t = \dfrac{K}{\sqrt{n}}$

When $t = 6$, $n = 8$ then $6 = \dfrac{K}{\sqrt{8}} \rightarrow K = 6.\sqrt{8}$

(Keep in this surd form until we need to calculate it.)

So when $n = 10$, $t = \dfrac{6\sqrt{8}}{\sqrt{10}} = 5.367$ hours, which will be 5 hours 22 minutes. However,

this time seems a bit too accurate, hence I would give the answer as $5\frac{1}{2}$ hours.

EXERCISE 3

The cost each for a party of youths to go to America for a Bruce Springstein concert varies inversely with the number of people in the party. When the original 25 booked the trip to America the cost each was £375. What will be the cost for each if three less go on the trip?

JOINT VARIATION

Joint variation is where three things (or more) vary with each other in combinations of direct and/or inverse proportion.

WORKED EXAMPLE 4

Heat, C, in calories in an electrically heated wire varies directly as the square of the voltage, v, directly as the time, t, and inversely as the resistance, r ohms. 57 calories are produced by 4 volts in 15 seconds for a wire with resistance of 20 ohms. How many calories will be produced in a wire with a resistance of 30 ohms, in 20 seconds by 10 volts?

Since $\quad C \propto \dfrac{v^2t}{r} \quad$ then $\quad C = \dfrac{Kv^2t}{r}$

$C = 57$ when $v = 4$, $t = 15$ and $r = 20$

hence $57 = \dfrac{K \times 16 \times 15}{20}$ and so $K = 4.75$.

So when $v = 10$, $t = 20$ and $r = 30$, $C = \dfrac{4.75 \times 100 \times 20}{30}$, which is 317 calories.

WORKED EXAMPLE 5

The volume of a cone varies jointly with the square of the base radius and the height. How will the volume change if the base radius is increased by 70% and the height decreased by 10%?

Since $V \propto r^2h$, then $V = Kr^2h$

So when $V = V_1$ $r = r_1$ and $h = h_1$, we start with $V_1 = Kr_1^2h_1$

So, if the radius is increased by 70%, $\qquad r_2 = 1.70r_1$

and if the height is decreased by 10%, $\qquad h_2 = 0.90h_1$

Hence $V_2 = K \times (1.7r_1)^2 \times (0.9h_1)$

$\qquad V_2 = 2.601\,Kr_1^2h_1 = 2.601\,V_1$

Hence the % increase is given by:

$\dfrac{(2.601\,V_1 - V_1)}{V_1} \times 100 = \dfrac{(2.601 - 1)V_1}{V_1} \times 100 = 160.1\%$

Hence the percentage increase is 160%.

(Yes, you should really have noted this straight from the $V_2 = 2.601V_1$, but I wanted it to be made clear to those with any doubts.)

EXERCISE 4

It was noted in a botanical garden that during the summer the number of insects in flight per m^3 in the greenhouse is directly proportional to the temperature and inversely proportional to the square root of the average centimetres of rainfall so far that summer.

It was noted early in the summer while the average rainfall was 0.3 cm per day, when the temperature was 16°C, there was an average of 4 insects in flight per m^3 in the greenhouse. If at the end of the summer it was noted that when the temperature was 12°C there were 2 insects in flight per m^3, what was the average rainfall for the summer?

SOLUTIONS TO EXERCISES

S1

The ratio of the areas is 15:20, which simplifies to 3:4, hence the ratio of lengths is $\sqrt{3}:\sqrt{4}$ which is $\sqrt{3}:2$. Hence the ratio of volumes is $(\sqrt{3})^3:2^3$ which is $(\sqrt{3})^3:8$.

So if the smaller tin contains 400 g, the larger tin will contain $400 \times \dfrac{8}{(\sqrt{3})^3} = 616$ g.

(*Note:* one of the simplest ways to evaluate $(\sqrt{3})^3$ on your calculator is to recognise $(\sqrt{3})^3 = 3^{1.5}$, then press the sequence of buttons $3 \rightarrow x^y \rightarrow 1.5 \rightarrow = $ to give 5.196 . . .)

S2

We note from the question that $p^2 \propto d^3$, hence $p^2 = Kd^3$ and for Earth, when $p = 365.25$, $d = 1.497 \times 10^8$, hence $(365.25)^2 = K(1.497 \times 10^8)^3$, so $K = 3.9766 \times 10^{-20}$ (kept in calculator memory).
So for Mercury, where $d = 5.8 \times 10^7$, $p^2 = K.d^3$
which gives $p^2 = K \times (5.8 \times 10^7)^3$
$$= 7758.9$$
$$p = \sqrt{7758.9} = 88.$$
Therefore the orbital period of Mercury is 88 days.

S3

Let number of youths in party $= Y$, the cost each be C, then
$$C \propto \frac{1}{Y} \text{ hence } \quad C = \frac{K}{Y}$$
When $Y = 25$, $C = 375$, so $375 = \dfrac{K}{25} \rightarrow K = 9375$

so when $Y = 22$, $C = \dfrac{9375}{22} = 426.14$.

The cost therefore is £426.14.

S4

From the question we note where I = insects in flight per m^3
$$t = \text{temperature } °C$$
$$r = \text{average cm of rainfall}$$

Then $I \propto \dfrac{t}{\sqrt{r}}$; hence $I = \dfrac{Kt}{\sqrt{r}}$

When $r = 0.3$, $t = 16$, $I = 4$

so $4 = \dfrac{K \times 16}{\sqrt{0.3}} \rightarrow K = \dfrac{4 \times \sqrt{0.3}}{16} = 0.137$.

So when $t = 12$ and $I = 2$, then $2 = \dfrac{0.137 \times 12}{\sqrt{r}}$

$\rightarrow \sqrt{r} = \dfrac{0.137 \times 12}{2} = 0.82$

$r = 0.675$ cm per day.

EXAM TYPE QUESTIONS

HIGHER LEVEL

Q1

The electrical resistance, R ohms, of a piece of wire of length one metre is inversely proportional to the square of its diameter, d cm. This can be written as $R = K\left(\dfrac{1}{d^n}\right)$.

a) State the value of n.

b) A metre length of copper wire has resistance of 5 ohms. Find the resistance of a piece of copper wire of the same length which has three times the diameter of the first piece.

(MEG; 1988)

Q2

Figure 6.3 shows a measuring scoop used for measuring soap powder for a washing machine. It has a diameter of 8 cm and a height of 10 cm.

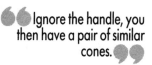

Ignore the handle, you then have a pair of similar cones.

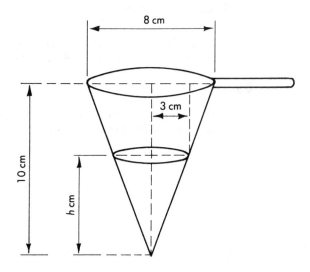

Fig. 6.3

Calculate the height of the powder (h cm) in the scoop when the radius of the soap powder surface is 3 cm.

(NEA; 1988)

Q3

The pressure needed to blow up the balloon in Fig. 6.4 varies as the cube of its radius. When the radius is 5 cm the pressure needed is 80 g/cm^2.

Fig. 6.4

a) What pressure is required when the radius is 15 cm?

b) What is the radius of the balloon when the pressure needed is 640 g/cm^2?

(WJEC; 1988)

Q4

Figure 6.5 shows two closed cylindrical cans, A and B. The radius of A is 4 cm and its height is 12 cm. The radius of B is 8 cm and its height is 6 cm.

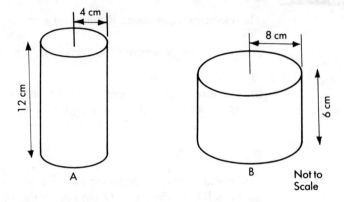

Fig. 6.5

a) Find, in the form 1:n, the ratio
   i) volume of A: volume of B
   ii) total surface area of A: total surface area of B.
b) Two cylinders have the same volume. The first has radius r and height h. If the radius of the second is $2r$, find its height in terms of h.   (MEG; 1988)

Q5

Figure 6.6, which is not drawn to scale, represents a symmetrical white sign fused on to a road with hot molten material. Angle BAC = 2 × angle DAE.

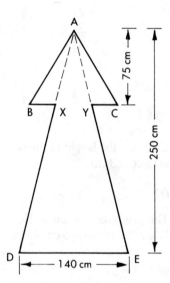

Fig. 6.6

In the following calculations, work to four significant figures and give answers to two significant figures.

a)   i) Use similar triangles to calculate the length XY.
     ii) Calculate the size of angle DAE.
     iii) Calculate the length BC.
     iv) Calculate the surface area of the sign.
b)   Each sign is 3 mm in depth and the material for 30 such signs can be poured from a full cylindrical boiler, 40 cm in depth.
     i) Calculate the volume of material used for each sign.
     ii) Calculate the internal radius of the boiler.   (NEA; 1988)

EXTENSION **Q6**

A variable t is inversely proportional to the square of p and varies directly with the cube root of q.

a) Find the change in t when:
   i) both p and q are doubled,
   ii) q is doubled and p is halved.
b) State the connection between the changes of p and q that would leave t unaltered, and quote a particular instance when this will be true (not when both are unaltered!).

OUTLINE ANSWERS TO EXAM QUESTIONS

A1

a) $n = 2$
b) Let the diameter of the first piece of wire be called d_1, then the diameter of the second piece of wire will be $3d_1$. So, for the first piece of wire we can state $5 = K\left(\dfrac{1}{d_1{}^2}\right)$

$\rightarrow K = 5\,d_1{}^2$

Hence for the second piece of wire $R = K\left(\dfrac{1}{(3d_1)^2}\right) = 5d_1{}^2 \times \dfrac{1}{9d_1{}^2}$

$R = \dfrac{5}{9}$ ohms

A2

Draw a simple sketch as in Fig. 6.7 to illustrate a pair of similar triangles. Then we can write down $\dfrac{h}{3} = \dfrac{10}{4}$

$\rightarrow h = \dfrac{30}{4} = 7.5$ cm.

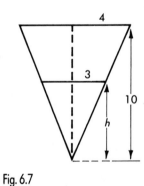

Fig. 6.7

A3

From the question $p \propto r^3$; hence $p = Kr^3$

When $r = 5$, $p = 80$, so $80 = K \times 125 \rightarrow K = \dfrac{80}{125} = 0.64$.

a) When $r = 15$, $p = 0.64 \times 15^3 = 2160$ g/cm^2
b) When $p = 640$, $640 = 0.64 \times r^3$
   hence $r^3 = 640 \div 0.64 = 1000$
   $r = \sqrt[3]{1000} = 10$
   $r = 10$ cm.

A4

a) i) Volume of A $= \pi r^2 h = \pi \times 16 \times 12 = 192\pi$
      Volume of B $= \pi r^2 h = \pi \times 64 \times 6 = 384\pi$
      Hence volume A : volume B $= 192\pi : 384\pi$
      $= 1 \quad : \dfrac{384\pi}{192\pi}$
      $= 1 \quad : \quad 2$

ii) Total surface area of A $= 2 \times \pi r^2 + 2\pi rh = (2 \times \pi \times 16) + (2 \times \pi \times 4 \times 12)$
$\qquad\qquad\qquad\qquad = 32\pi + 96\pi \qquad\quad = 128\pi$
$\qquad$ Total surface area of B $= 2\pi r^2 + 2\pi rh \quad = (2 \times \pi \times 64) + (2 \times \pi \times 8 \times 6)$
$\qquad\qquad\qquad\qquad = 128\pi + 96\pi \qquad = 224\pi$
$\qquad$ ratio of surf' area of A : surf' area of B $= 128\pi : 224\pi$

$$= 1 : \frac{224\pi}{128\pi}$$

$$= 1 : 1.75$$

b) Volume $= \pi r^2 h$.

So if another cylinder of same volume, yet radius $2r$, let h be h_1,

then $\pi r^2 h = \pi (2r)^2 h_1$

$\rightarrow \quad \pi r^2 h = 4\pi r^2 h_1$

$\rightarrow \quad \dfrac{\pi r^2 h}{4\pi r^2} = h_1 \rightarrow h_1 = \dfrac{h}{4}.$

A5

a) i) $\dfrac{XY}{140} = \dfrac{75}{250} \rightarrow \quad XY = \dfrac{75 \times 140}{250} = 42$ cm.

ii) Sketch the triangle ADE as shown in Fig. 6.8 with P the foot of the perpendicular from A.

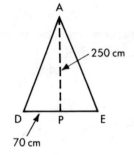

Then $\tan D\hat{A}P = \dfrac{70}{250} = 0.28$

$\rightarrow D\hat{A}P \qquad = 15.64$

Hence $D\hat{A}E = 2 \times D\hat{A}P = 31°$ (to two significant figures).

iii) In Fig. 6.9, since $B\hat{A}C = 2 \times D\hat{A}E$, then $B\hat{A}C = 62.57$ (to 4 sig. figs.). So when T is the foot of the perpendicular from A, then $C\hat{A}T = 31.28°$.

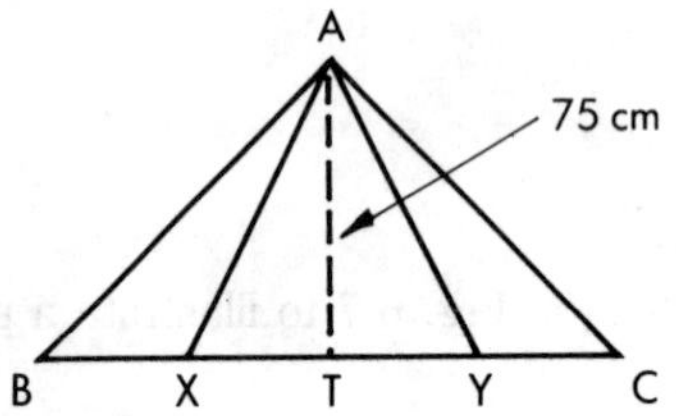

A

250 cm

D   P   E

70 cm

Fig. 6.8

75 cm

Fig. 6.9

Hence $\dfrac{TC}{75} = \tan 31.28$

$\rightarrow$ TC $= 75 \tan 31.28° = 45.57$.

Hence BC $= 2 \times$ TC $= 91$ cm   (to 2 sig. figs.)

iv) Find area of three triangles ABX, ACY (which are the same area) and ADE.

Area of ABX $= \frac{1}{2}$base $\times$ height $= \frac{1}{2} \times$ (TC $-$ TY) $\times 75$
$\qquad\qquad\qquad\qquad = \frac{1}{2} \times (24.57) \times 75 = 921.5$ cm^2 (4 sig. figs.)

Hence ABX $+$ ACY $= 921.5 \times 2 \quad = 1843$ cm^2 (4 sig. figs.)

Area of ADE $= \frac{1}{2} \times 140 \times 250 \quad = 17500$ cm^2

Total area $=$ ABX $+$ ACY $+$ ADE $= 19000$ cm^2 (2 sig. figs.)

b) i) Volume for each sign will be a) iv) $\times 3$ mm, which is $19343 \times 0.3 = 5802.9$ cm^3, which is 5800 cm^3 (2 sig. figs.)

ii) Volume of cylinder up to height 40 cm will be given by $30 \times$ b) i) $= 174087$ cm^3 (as accurate as possible). Volume of cylinder given by $\pi r^2 h$

then $\pi r^2 \times 40 = 174087$

$\rightarrow r^2 \qquad = \dfrac{174087}{40\pi} = 1385.34$

$\rightarrow r \qquad = 37$ cm (2 sig. figs.)

A6

a) Since $t \propto \dfrac{\sqrt[3]{q}}{p^2}$ then $t = \dfrac{K\sqrt[3]{q}}{p^2}$

i) If $t_0 = \dfrac{K\sqrt[3]{q_0}}{p_0^2}$ then where p_0 and q_0 are both doubled

$$t_1 = \frac{K\sqrt[3]{2q_0}}{(2p_0)^2} = \frac{K\sqrt[3]{2}\cdot\sqrt[3]{q_0}}{4p_0^2} = \frac{\sqrt[3]{2}}{4}\cdot\frac{K\sqrt[3]{q_0}}{p_0^2} = \frac{\sqrt[3]{2}}{4}t_0$$

$$t_1 = 0.315\, t_0$$

so t has been reduced by $(100-31.5)\%$, which is a reduction of 68.5%.

ii) If $t_0 = \dfrac{K\sqrt[3]{q_0}}{p_0^2}$ then where q_0 is doubled, and p_0 is halved,

$$t_1 = \frac{K\sqrt[3]{2q_0}}{(\frac{1}{2}p_0)^2} = \frac{\sqrt[3]{2}}{\frac{1}{4}}\cdot\frac{K\sqrt[3]{q_0}}{p_0^2} = 5.04\, t_0$$

so t has been increased by $(504-100)\%$ which is an increase of 404%.

b) Let increase in $q = x\%$ and increase in $p = y\%$

then where $t_0 = \dfrac{K\sqrt[3]{q_0}}{p_0^2}$, $t_1 = \dfrac{K\sqrt[3]{\left(1+\dfrac{x}{100}\right)q_0}}{\left(\left(1+\dfrac{y}{100}\right)p_0\right)^2} = \dfrac{\sqrt[3]{\left(1+\dfrac{x}{100}\right)}}{\left(1+\dfrac{y}{100}\right)^2}\cdot\dfrac{K\sqrt[3]{q_0}}{p_0^2}$

when $t_0 = t_1$, then $\sqrt[3]{\left(1+\dfrac{x}{100}\right)} = \left(1+\dfrac{y}{100}\right)^2$

hence $\left(1+\dfrac{x}{100}\right) = \left(1+\dfrac{y}{100}\right)^6$

so there is no change when the increase in q is $x\%$ and of p is $y\%$

and $\left(1+\dfrac{x}{100}\right) = \left(1+\dfrac{y}{100}\right)^6$

So, for example, if the increase in q is 50%, then

$$1.50 = \left(1+\dfrac{y}{100}\right)^6$$

$$1.0699 = 1+\dfrac{y}{100} \rightarrow y = 7\%\text{ increase.}$$

i.e. when q is increased by 50% and p is increased by 7%, then t is unaltered.

A STUDENT'S ANSWER
WITH EXAMINER'S COMMENTS

Question

Jean and Bill use a set of scales to weigh some coins. They have four 50p coins whose total weight is 5 grams and two 20p coins whose total weight is 1 gram.

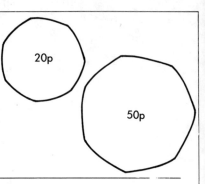

a)   i)   Make an estimate of the weight of a 50p coin and of a 20p coin.

$5 \div 4 = 1.25$

$1 \div 2 = 0.5$

The 50p will weigh 1.25

the 20p will weigh 0.5

> 66 Correct working, but no units given on the final answer, this will lose marks. 99

ii)   Which estimate is likely to be the more accurate and why?

the 50p because you used more coins.

> 66 Correct answer, but answer is brief and more explanation is needed. 99

b)   A slot through which a 50p coin will just pass is 3.0 cm long. A 20p coin will just pass through a slot 2.1 cm long. The *faces* of the two coins have the same shape. Find the ratio of the areas of the faces of a 50p coin and a 20p coin in the form $n : 1$.

50p Coins Only   20p Coins Only

3.0 cm   2.1 cm

ratio of lengths is $3.0 : 2.1$

> 66 Living dangerously here, fortunately the next line shows the student's intent to square each part of the ratio, but this should have been made clear here. 99

ratio of areas $= 3.0 : 2.1^{2}$

$= 9 : 4.41$

$\simeq 2.04 : 1$

c)   The 50p coin is 2.5 mm thick. Assuming that both coins are made of the same metal, calculate an estimate of the thickness of a 20p coin.

We know that weight $\propto$ area $\times$ width, so weight $= k$ area $\times$ width

let area of 50p $= 2.04$ and area of 20p $= 1$

For 50p then $1.25 = k \times 2.04 \times 2.5$, $k = 0.245$

For 20p then $0.5 = 0.245 \times 1 \times$ width

width $= 2.04$ mm

> 66 A good, sound method, but the final answer is too precise for an estimate. 2mm would be the best answer. 99

GETTING STARTED

Algebra and how you use it is perhaps the key 'thing' that makes mathematicians a grade A or a grade C! Up to grade C, algebra is informal and is mainly concerned with simple situations. At the higher grades and beyond, algebra is an integral part of many situations, as you will already have seen.

You must understand and be able to cope confidently with algebra. This chapter is about how you should be manipulating your algebraic terms and expressions.

USEFUL DEFINITIONS

Coefficient	The whole number next to a variable, e.g. the coefficient of x^2 in $3x^2$ is the 3.
Constant	Not changing.
Domain	The set of numbers from which a mapping or function is applied.
Expand	To multiply out brackets and simplify.
Factorise	Put into expressions containing brackets that multiply together to make the whole.
Function	An algebraic rule for changing one number to another, where each number will only have one unique image.
Generalise	Express in general terms, usually an algebraic formula.
Image	The number that is arrived at from another by some particular function.
Linear	An expression involving only single variables of power one, e.g. $x + y = 3$ or $2x = y + 7$.
Quadratic	An expression involving no power higher than a squared term, e.g. $5x^2 - 3x = 4$.
Range	The set of numbers to which a mapping or function form the image of a given domain.
Simplify	To make easier, usually in algebra means to collect like terms or cancel.
Transposition	To change the subject of a formula or equation.
Variable	A letter which may stand for various numbers.

ESSENTIAL PRINCIPLES

1 >TRANSPOSITION

> This is your basic rule to follow, learn it and use it.

All your manipulation of algebra lies in being able to understand the principle of:

If it's doing what it's doing to everything else on that side of the equation, then it can be moved to the other side and perform the opposite job.

Follow through the following changes of subject of formula and then try them yourself to make absolutely certain that you can confidently cope with this basic requirement of algebra.

WORKED EXAMPLE 1

Change $x = 5y - 7$ to make y the subject.

$$x + 7 = 5y$$
$$\rightarrow \frac{x+7}{5} = y; \text{ hence } y = \frac{x+7}{5}$$

WORKED EXAMPLE 2

Change $p = \frac{t}{4} + 7$ to make t the subject.

$$p - 7 = \frac{t}{4}$$
$$\rightarrow 4(p - 7) = t; \text{ hence } t = 4(p - 7)$$

WORKED EXAMPLE 3

Change $v = p(4t+1)$ to make t the subject.

$$\frac{v}{p} = 4t+1$$
$$\rightarrow \frac{v}{p} - 1 = 4t$$
$$\rightarrow \frac{v-p}{p} = 4t \quad \text{(easier to cope with if we simplify the LHS)}$$
$$\rightarrow \frac{v-p}{4p} = t$$

WORKED EXAMPLE 4

Change $t = \frac{3w+4}{5-w}$ to make w the subject.

$$t(5-w) = 3w+4$$
$$5t-wt = 3w+4 \quad \rightarrow 5t-4 = 3w+wt$$
$$\rightarrow 5t-4 = w(3+t)$$
$$\rightarrow \frac{5t-4}{3+t} = w$$

hence $w = \dfrac{5t-4}{3+t}$

WORKED EXAMPLE 5

Change $x = y^2 - 7$ to make y the subject.
$$x+7 = y^2 \rightarrow \sqrt{(x+7)} = y$$
hence $y = \sqrt{(x+7)}$

<table>
<tr><td>**2**</td><td>**LINEAR EQUATIONS**</td></tr>
</table>

Linear equations are equations that involve single variables of power 1. They contain no expressions such as x^2, y^3, $\frac{1}{x}$, xy, etc.

You should be familiar with linear equations and how to solve them. You move numbers around *until* you have the unknown as the subject, then do any necessary calculations.

<table>
<tr><td>**WORKED EXAMPLE 6**</td></tr>
</table>

Solve the equation $8 = \dfrac{x+5}{5-x}$

Change first to $8(5 - x) = x + 5$

$$\rightarrow 40 - 8x = x + 5$$
$$\rightarrow 40 - 5 = x + 8x = 9x$$
$$\rightarrow \frac{35}{9} = x$$
$$x = 3.9 \text{ (1 decimal place)}$$

EXERCISE 1

Solve the equation $\dfrac{x - 3}{x + 3} = 3$

<table>
<tr><td>**3**</td><td>**QUADRATIC EQUATIONS**</td></tr>
</table>

Quadratic equations are those that involve no higher power than a 2, nor any less than a 1. For example, $3x^2 + 6x - 1 = 0$.

They can be solved in a number of different ways depending on the particular combination of numbers they contain.

66 In the exam it will not matter which way you have solved it, as long as the method is clearly shown, and it helps if the answer is right! 99

SIMPLE FACTORISATION

There are times (and generally these are the only ones you are likely to be asked in the GCSE examination), when the quadratic equation will go nicely into two brackets to solve.

<table>
<tr><td>**WORKED EXAMPLE 7**</td></tr>
</table>

Solve the equation $6x^2 + 5x - 6 = 0$.

Factorise by trying to put into two brackets ( )( ). The -6 indicates that the signs are different, hence (+)(−). Now the first number in each bracket (the coefficients of x) must multiply to give 6, whilst the end two constants in each bracket must also multiply together to give 6. This gives us quite a few possibilities, eg. $(2x + 2)(3x - 3)$, but the *combination* of the outer two and the inner two must give us $+5x$. In effect we have the choices given by:

$$\left(\begin{smallmatrix}6\\1\end{smallmatrix} \times \begin{smallmatrix}6\\1\end{smallmatrix}\right), \left(\begin{smallmatrix}6\\1\end{smallmatrix} \times \begin{smallmatrix}1\\6\end{smallmatrix}\right), \left(\begin{smallmatrix}6\\1\end{smallmatrix} \times \begin{smallmatrix}2\\3\end{smallmatrix}\right), \left(\begin{smallmatrix}6\\1\end{smallmatrix} \times \begin{smallmatrix}3\\2\end{smallmatrix}\right), \left(\begin{smallmatrix}3\\2\end{smallmatrix} \times \begin{smallmatrix}6\\1\end{smallmatrix}\right), \left(\begin{smallmatrix}3\\2\end{smallmatrix} \times \begin{smallmatrix}1\\6\end{smallmatrix}\right), \left(\begin{smallmatrix}3\\2\end{smallmatrix} \times \begin{smallmatrix}2\\3\end{smallmatrix}\right), \left(\begin{smallmatrix}3\\2\end{smallmatrix} \times \begin{smallmatrix}3\\2\end{smallmatrix}\right)$$

but where the difference in the diagonals must give us 5. This is done in the combination

$$\left(\begin{smallmatrix}3\\2\end{smallmatrix} \times \begin{smallmatrix}2\\3\end{smallmatrix}\right) \quad \text{i.e. } (3 \times 3) - (2 \times 2) = 9 - 4 = 5.$$

So the factorisation is $(3x - 2)(2x + 3)$, the positive with the largest combination, since the $5x$ is positive.

So $(3x - 2)(2x + 3) = 0$

which gives us $3x - 2 = 0$ and $2x + 3 = 0$

$$3x = 2 \qquad\qquad 2x = -3$$
$$x = \frac{2}{3} \text{ and} \qquad x = \frac{-3}{2}$$

Solution is $x = \dfrac{2}{3}$ and $\dfrac{-3}{2}$

This method works very well when your solution gives two brackets with integers in them, and when you happen to 'spot' the right combination. Try the following exercise.

EXERCISE 2

Solve the equations   i) $30x^2 + 19x - 4 = 0$;   ii) $12x^2 + x - 6 = 0$.

COMPLETING THE SQUARE

You may have done that last exercise quite quickly, or you may have taken quite a time to solve it. It can be a quick method, but only if you *spot* the connection and even then only if the thing does give two nice brackets.

Another way of always finding a solution (if there is one) is the method of *completing the square*. This follows through the simple procedure:

$$ax^2 + bx + c = 0$$

Divide throughout by 'a' to give $x^2 + \dfrac{b}{a}x + \dfrac{c}{a} = 0$.

Move the constant term to the other side, to give $x^2 + \dfrac{b}{a}x = -\dfrac{c}{a}$

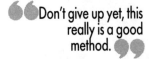
Don't give up yet, this really is a good method.

Now halve the coefficient of x to make $\left(x + \dfrac{b}{2a}\right)^2 = -\dfrac{c}{a} + \left(\dfrac{b}{2a}\right)^2$, which will now have given you an equation like

$$(x+d)^2 = e$$
$$\rightarrow x+d = +\sqrt{e} \text{ and } -\sqrt{e}$$
$$\rightarrow x = +\sqrt{e}-d \text{ and } -\sqrt{e}-d.$$

It looks worse than it actually is. Follow through worked example 8, then try this method in exercise 3; then try it again in exercise 2 above.

WORKED EXAMPLE 8

Solve the equation $2x^2 + 5x - 3 = 0$.

Divide throughout by 2 to give $x^2 + \dfrac{5x}{2} - \dfrac{3}{2} = 0$.

$$\left(x+\dfrac{5}{4}\right)^2 = \dfrac{3}{2} + \dfrac{25}{16} \text{ (look where things have come from)}$$

hence $\left(x+\dfrac{5}{4}\right)^2 = 3.0625$

$$\rightarrow x+\dfrac{5}{4} = 1.75 \text{ and } -1.75$$

$$x = (1.75-1.25) \text{ and } (-1.75-1.25)$$
$$= 0.5 \text{ and } -3$$
$$x = 0.5 \text{ and } -3.$$

EXERCISE 3

Solve the equations   i) $6x^2 + 7x + 2 = 9$;   ii) $2x^2 - x - 6 = 0$.

Of course this method is only useful when solving and not when just factorising, when you do need two complete brackets, but it is worth familiarising yourself with the method.

SOLVE BY THE FORMULA

There is a well known, loved and trusted *formula* which will also always work to solve equations of the type $ax^2 + bx + c = 0$.

This is $x = \dfrac{-b \pm \sqrt{b^2 - 4ac}}{2a}$

(it is the formal next stage to completing the square).

WORKED EXAMPLE 9

Solve the equation $2x^2 + 5x - 3 = 0$.

Using $x = \dfrac{-b \pm \sqrt{(b^2 - 4ac)}}{2a}$, where $a = 2, b = 5$ and $c = -3$

then $x = \dfrac{-5 \pm \sqrt{(25 + 24)}}{4} = \dfrac{-5 \pm \sqrt{(49)}}{4} = \dfrac{-5 \pm 7}{4}$

$x = \dfrac{-12}{4}$ and $\dfrac{2}{4}$

$x = -3$ and 0.5.

Try this method on the exercises 2 and 3 if you wish to compare. All three methods are good and useful. You need to use the method that you are most confident with, or which best suits the situation at the time.

DIFFERENCE OF TWO SQUARES

When we have an expression that is made up of two square expressions (or numbers) and subtracted, then they can **always** be factorised as:

$$A^2x^2 - B^2y^2 = (Ax + By)(Ax - By).$$

WORKED EXAMPLE 10

Factorise the equation $16x^2 - 9y^2$

$16x^2 - 9y^2 = (4x + 3y)(4x - 3y)$.

EXERCISE 4

Factorise the expressions   i) $9t^2 - 4p^2$;   ii) $4x^4 - 9y^2$.

4 ▷ SIMULTANEOUS EQUATIONS

> 66 These will often appear with equations in words instead of normal equations. 99

Simultaneous equations are pairs of equations that contain more than one variable and need solving at the same time. They are often linear, but they do not both need to be so. There are two basic techniques for solving them, the *elimination method* and the *substitution method*.

ELIMINATION METHOD

You eliminate one variable, solve the remaining equation then substitute back into one equation to find the final solution.

WORKED EXAMPLE 11

Solve simultaneously the equations: $4x - 2y = 11 \ldots (1)$
$3x + y = 12 \ldots (2)$
Multiply equation (2) through by 2 to enable us to eliminate y.

$4x - 2y = 11 \ldots (1)$
$6x + 2y = 24 \ldots (3)$
Adding the two equations eliminates y

hence $10x = 35$
$\rightarrow \quad x = 3.5$

Substitute $x = 3.5$ into equation (1)

$14 - 2y = 11$
$\rightarrow \quad 2y = 3$
$y = 1.5$

It is usual to check the solution by substituting into the other equation, this time equation (2) to give $(3 \times 3.5) + 1.5 = 12$ which is correct; so the solution is $x = 3.5, y = 1.5$.

EXERCISE 5

Solve the pair of simultaneous equations

$2x + 3y = 10$
$6x - y = 5$

SUBSTITUTION METHOD

Let's use the same simultaneous equations as in the previous part

$$4x - 2y = 11 \ldots (1)$$
$$3x + y = 12 \ldots (2)$$

Then from (2), $y = 12 - 3x$. Now substitute this into equation (1) to give

$$
\begin{aligned}
4x - 2(12 - 3x) &= 11 \\
\rightarrow \quad 4x - 24 + 6x &= 11 \\
\rightarrow \quad 10x &= 35 \\
\rightarrow \quad x &= 3.5
\end{aligned}
$$

and we are where we arrived at before; we now need to substitute $x = 3.5$ into one of the equations to complete the solution.

This method really becomes more useful when only one equation is linear.

WORKED EXAMPLE 12

Solve the simultaneous equations $x^2 + y = 8 \ldots (1)$
$$x - 3y = 1 \ldots (2)$$

From equation (1), $y = 8 - x^2$, so substitute into equation (2) to give

$$x - 3(8 - x^2) = 1$$
$$x - 24 + 3x^2 = 1$$
$$3x^2 + x - 25 = 0$$

Which is a *quadratic* equation and can be solved by one of the previous methods to give $x = 2.72$ and $x = -3.06$ (2 decimal places). Substitute each into equation (1) which gives the final solution that

$$
\begin{aligned}
x &= 2.72; & y &= 0.60 \\
\text{and } x &= -3.06; & y &= -1.36
\end{aligned}
$$

EXERCISE 6

Solve the simultaneous equations $\quad x - y = 5 \ldots (1)$
$$x^2 + 2y = 24 \ldots (2)$$

---

5 ALGEBRAIC FRACTIONS

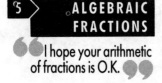
I hope your arithmetic of fractions is O.K.

You really must be confident with normal fraction arithmetic to stand a chance of being successful with *algebraic fractions*. This is because you have to apply the normal fraction rules without being able to resort to 'common fractions'.

ADDING AND SUBTRACTING

As in normal fractions you need a *common denominator*, after which you can either add or subtract.

WORKED EXAMPLE 13

Simplify $\dfrac{x}{2} + \dfrac{1}{x + 1} = 5$.

To get a common denominator on the left hand side multiply each fraction top and bottom by the numerator of the other fraction

hence $\dfrac{x(x + 1)}{2(x + 1)} + \dfrac{2 \times 1}{2(x + 1)} = 5$

$\rightarrow \dfrac{x(x + 1) + 2}{2(x + 1)} = 5$

$\rightarrow x(x + 1) + 2 = 10(x + 1)$

$\rightarrow x^2 + x + 2 = 10x + 10$

$\rightarrow x^2 - 9x - 8 = 0$

EXERCISE 7

Solve the equation $1 + \dfrac{1}{x} = x$

MULTIPLYING

It is the cancelling here that seems to mystify most people. You must remember that when *multiplying fractions* you can cancel any factor on the top with any factor on the bottom,

$$\frac{\cancel{2}^1}{3}\times\frac{5}{\cancel{6}_3} = \frac{5}{9}.$$

WORKED EXAMPLE 14

Factorise and hence simplify: $\dfrac{(x^2 - 5x + 4)}{(x^2 + x - 6)} \times \dfrac{(x^2 + 4x + 3)}{(x^2 - 2x - 8)}$

Factorise each quadratic to obtain $\dfrac{(x-4)(x-1)}{(x-2)(x+3)} \times \dfrac{(x+1)(x+3)}{(x-4)(x+2)}$

The $(x - 4)$ will cancel top and bottom, as will the $(x + 3)$, leaving the expression as

$\dfrac{(x - 1)(x + 1)}{(x - 2)(x + 2)}$ which is $\dfrac{x^2 - 1}{x^2 - 4}$

DIVIDING

Remember the rule to turn the second fraction upside down and multiply.

WORKED EXAMPLE 15

Solve $\dfrac{(x + 1)}{3} \div \dfrac{4}{(x + 1)} = 1$

Turn the second fraction upside down and multiply, which gives us

$$\frac{(x+1)}{3}\times\frac{(x+1)}{4} = 1$$

$$\begin{aligned}
\to (x+1)^2 &= 12 \\
\to x+1 &= \sqrt{12} = 3.46 \text{ and } -3.46 \\
x &= 3.46-1 \text{ and } -3.46-1 \\
x &= 2.46 \text{ and } -4.46
\end{aligned}$$

EXERCISE 8

Find i) the product;   ii) the quotient of $\dfrac{x + 1}{x - 1}$ and $\dfrac{x^2 - 1}{x^2 + 1}$

6 ▷ FRACTIONAL INDICES

The use of the *fractional index* is used to denote a root,

e.g. $9^{1/2} = \sqrt{9} = 3$ and -3
     $8^{1/3} = \sqrt[3]{8} = 2$

NB. $8^{2/3} = (\sqrt[3]{8})^2 = 2^2 = 4$ **or** $\sqrt[3]{8^2} = \sqrt[3]{64} = 4$

Use the $x^{\frac{1}{y}}$ button on your calculator to calculate the answers. For example, to calculate $9^{\frac{1}{5}}$, just press 9 followed by $x^{\frac{1}{y}}$, followed by 5 =   , this should give you 1.55.

Similarly, if you need to calculate a cube root, maybe from a similar shape situation, then use the $x^{\frac{1}{y}}$ button on your calculator followed by a 3.

❝❝Do work all these out on the calculator with the correct buttons ... it's so much easier. ❞❞

WORKED EXAMPLE 16

Which is the larger? $18^{2/3}$ or $8^{3/2}$
$18^{2/3} = (\sqrt[3]{18})^2 = 6.868$
$8^{\frac{3}{2}} = (\sqrt{8})^3 = 22.63$
hence $8^{\frac{3}{2}} > 18^{2/3}$

EXERCISE 9

Calculate i) $5^{\frac{2}{5}}$; ii) $\sqrt[3]{11}$; iii) $8^{-0.7}$

7 ▷ FUNCTIONS AND THEIR COMBINATIONS

The only *functions* we are going to consider are *algebraic functions* which give a rule for changing one number to another.

For example f : $x \to 3x$ is the function f were any number is multiplied by 3 to obtain its image. Another way of denoting the same function is to say f(x) = $3x$.

WORKED EXAMPLE 17

For the function f : $x \to \sin(2x)$ find f(40).

$f(40) = \sin(2 \times 40) = \sin 80 = 0.9848$.

EXERCISE 10

Where f : $x \to (x-1)^2$, what is   i) f(1);   ii) f(0);   iii) f(−1).

DOMAIN AND RANGE

The set of numbers that the given function is applied to is called the *domain*. The set of numbers that the function takes numbers to is called the *range*.

WORKED EXAMPLE 18

If the domain of the function f:$x \to \dfrac{1}{x+1}$ is $\{x:2 \leqslant x \leqslant 10\}$ find the range of the function.

We need to find all the possible images from x between 2 and 10 inclusive. Looking at the function tells us that as x gets bigger then so f(x) gets gradually smaller.

Hence f(2) will give the upper limit of the range f(2) $= \dfrac{1}{3}$

and f(10) will give the lower limit of the range f(10) $= \dfrac{1}{11}$

so the range will be $\left\{x:\dfrac{1}{11} \leqslant x \leqslant \dfrac{1}{3}\right\}$

WHEN IS A FUNCTION NOT A FUNCTION?

The question should really be 'when is an algebraic rule that looks like a function not really a function?'.

A mathematical function, f, must have for each x in the domain one, and only one, possible image f(x).

For example f:$x \to \sqrt{x}$ is *not* a mathematical function since the $\sqrt{x}$ will have two possible values, the negative and the positive square root of x.

INVERSE FUNCTIONS

The inverse of a function is that function that will return each number from the range back to its origin in the domain. It can be thought of as the function 'the opposite way round'.

The notation of an inverse function of f(x) is usually $f^{-1}(x)$.

There are a number of ways of finding an inverse to a function, some of these can quite readily be seen, for example:

If f(x) = x + 3   then $f^{-1}(x) = x - 3$
If f(x) = 6x then $f^{-1}(x) = \dfrac{6}{x}$

Others, like f(x) $= \dfrac{3x+1}{1-x}$ are not quite so easily spotted, and we need a procedure to find

them. But first we just need to look at *self inverses*.

A function has a self inverse when the same function will return each number in an image back to the original number in the domain. Try the following for yourself and see that they are *all* self inverses.

If f(x) $= \dfrac{1}{x}$ then $f^{-1}(x) = \dfrac{1}{x}$
If f(x) $= \dfrac{24}{x}$ then $f^{-1}(x) = \dfrac{24}{x}$
If f(x) = 10 − x then $f^{-1}(x) = 10 - x$.

Hence the type of functions f:$x \to \dfrac{A}{x}$ and f:$x \to A-x$ when A is a real number are *all* self inverses.

A rule to find inverses

There are two ways of finding inverses, and each, at times, is better than the other. Look at both, and become familiar with both, so that when an inverse is needed, you are equipped to choose the best method for finding the inverse in that specific case.

Flow diagram method

State the function as a *flow diagram*, or sequence of simple steps from x to f(x), then write down the reverse process and put it into function form.

> **WORKED EXAMPLE 19**

Find the inverse function of $f : x \to 5 + \dfrac{3}{(x-1)}$

Write as a flow diagram starting with x.

Start $\to$ subtract 1 $\to$ divide into 3 $\to$ add on 5 $\to$ end

$$x \to (x-1) \to \frac{3}{(x-1)} \to 5 + \frac{3}{(x-1)} = f(x).$$

Now the inverse will come back the other way, doing the inverse operations, starting with x

end $\leftarrow$ add 1 $\leftarrow$ divide into 3 $\leftarrow$ subtract 5 $\leftarrow$ start

$$f^{-1}(x) \leftarrow 1 + \frac{3}{(x-5)} \leftarrow \frac{3}{(x-5)} \leftarrow (x-5) \leftarrow x$$

hence inverse given by $f^{-1} : x \to 1 + \dfrac{3}{(x-5)}$

EXERCISE 11

Find the inverse of the following functions and state which inverse is not a function.

i) $f : x \to \dfrac{4-x}{5}$; ii) $g : x \to \dfrac{6x-10}{3}$; iii) $h : x \to x^2 + 1$

Transposition method

This method has the advantage over the previous one in that it will *always* work and is better suited to the more complicated functions.

It is dependent on rewriting the function as an algebraic equation and then transposing the equation to make x the subject. Follow through the worked example.

> **WORKED EXAMPLE 20**

Find the inverse function of $f : x \to \dfrac{3x+1}{1-x}$

Rewrite as $y = \dfrac{3x+1}{1-x}$ then transpose to make x the subject.

$$\to y(1-x) = 3x + 1$$
$$\to y - yx = 3x + 1 \to y - 1 = 3x + yx$$
$$\to y - 1 = x(3+y) \to \frac{y-1}{3+y} = x$$

So the inverse function is $f^{-1} : x \to \dfrac{x-1}{3+x}$

(note how to write down the inverse function we need to replace the y with the x again).

EXERCISE 12

Find the inverse functions of   i) $f : x \to \dfrac{x}{4+x}$; ii) $g(x) = \dfrac{x+1}{1-x}$

COMBINATION FUNCTIONS

When we combine two or more functions together we usually call them *composite functions.* For example, if we have two functions f and g such that $f:x \rightarrow 6x + 1$ $g:x \rightarrow \dfrac{x-2}{3}$

then fg(x) is the composite function of f and g together, where g is applied first, then f.

Hence $fg(x) = f\left(\dfrac{x-2}{3}\right) = 6\left(\dfrac{x-2}{3}\right) + 1 = 2(x-2) + 1 = 2x - 3.$

It should be noted that fg(x) and gf(x) are the different way round and will nearly always give a *different* composite function. For example, using the same f and g as above:

$$gf(x) = g(6x + 1) = \dfrac{(6x + 1) - 2}{3} = \dfrac{6x - 1}{3}$$

and so you see an example where gf(x) does not equal fg(x).

WORKED EXAMPLE 21

Where $f(x) = 2x + 1$ and $g(x) = x^2$, find the values of x such that $fg(x) = gf(x)$.

$fg(x) = f(x^2) = 2x^2 + 1$
$gf(x) = g(2x + 1) = (2x + 1)^2 = 4x^2 + 4x + 1.$

When fg(x) = gf(x) then $2x^2 + 1 = 4x^2 + 4x + 1$

$\rightarrow 0 = 2x^2 + 4x$
$\rightarrow 2x(x + 2) = 0$
$\rightarrow x = 0$ and $x = -2.$

Hence fg(x) = gf(x) when $x = 0$ and $x = -2.$

EXERCISE 13

Where $f:x \rightarrow \dfrac{1+x}{x}$ and $g:x \rightarrow 1 + x$, find   i) fg(x);   ii) gf(x)

SOLUTIONS TO EXERCISES

S1

$x - 3 = 3(x + 3) \rightarrow x - 3 = 3x + 9 \rightarrow -3 - 9 = 3x - x$
$\qquad\qquad\qquad \rightarrow -12 = 2x \qquad\qquad \rightarrow -6 = x \rightarrow x = -6$

S2

i) $(6x-1)(5x+4)$
$\rightarrow 6x-1 = 0$ and $5x+4 = 0$

$x = \dfrac{1}{6}$ and $x = \dfrac{-4}{5}$

ii) $(4x+3)(3x-2)$
$\rightarrow 4x+3 = 0$ and $3x-2 = 0$

$x = \dfrac{-3}{4}$ and $x = \dfrac{2}{3}$

S3

i) $x = -0.67$ and -0.5;   ii) $x = -1.5$ and 2

S4

i) $(3t + 2p))(3t - 2p)$;   ii) $(2x^2 + 3y)(2x^2 - 3y)$

S5

Eliminate y first to obtain $x = 1.25$, then substitute in one of the equations to give $y = 2.5.$

S6

From equation (1) $x = 5 + y$, substitute this into equation (2) to give $(5 + y)^2 + 2y = 24$

$\rightarrow 25 + 10y + y^2 + 2y = 24$
$\rightarrow y^2 + 12y + 1 \qquad = 0$

This will solve to give $y = -0.08$ and -11.9.
So from equation (1) we can now give the full solution of

$$x = 4.92, \ y = -0.08$$
$$\text{and } x = -6.9, y = -11.9.$$

S7

Find a common denominator x to give $\dfrac{x}{x} + \dfrac{1}{x} = x$

$$\rightarrow \frac{x + 1}{x} = x \rightarrow x + 1 = x^2 \rightarrow x^2 - x - 1 = 0$$

This will solve to give 1.62 and -0.62.

S8

i) product $= \dfrac{(x+1)}{(x-1)} \times \dfrac{(x^2-1)}{(x^2+1)} = \dfrac{(x+1)}{\cancel{(x-1)}} \times \dfrac{(x+1)\,\cancel{(x-1)}}{(x^2+1)} = \dfrac{(x+1)^2}{(x^2+1)}$

ii) quotient $= \dfrac{(x+1)}{(x-1)} \div \dfrac{(x^2-1)}{(x^2+1)} = \dfrac{(x+1)}{(x-1)} \times \dfrac{(x^2+1)}{(x+1)\,(x-1)} = \dfrac{x^2+1}{(x-1)^2}$

S9

i) Use calculator as $5 \rightarrow x^y \rightarrow 0.4$ (i.e. $^2/_5$) $= 1.9$
ii) Use calculator as $11 \rightarrow x^{\frac{1}{y}} \rightarrow 3 = 2.22$
iii) Use calculator as $8 \rightarrow x^y \rightarrow 0.7 \rightarrow {}^+/_- = 0.23$
Do try to become familiar with the use of x^y and $x^{\frac{1}{y}}$ buttons on your calculator.

S10

i) $f(1) = 0$; ii) $f(0) = 1$; iii) $f(-1) = 4$.

S11

i) $f^{-2}:x \rightarrow 4-5x$; ii) $f^{-1}:x \rightarrow \dfrac{3x+10}{6}$; iii) $f^{-1}:x \rightarrow \sqrt{(x-1)}$.

The last one is not a function since each image has two possibilities.

S12

i) $f^{-1}:x \rightarrow \dfrac{4x}{1-x}$; ii) $f^{-1}:x \rightarrow \dfrac{x-1}{x+1}$

S13

i) $fg(x) = f(1+x) = \dfrac{1+(1+x)}{(1+x)} = \dfrac{2+x}{1+x}$

ii) $gf(x) = g\left(\dfrac{1+x}{x}\right) = 1+\left(\dfrac{1+x}{x}\right) = \dfrac{x+1+x}{x} = \dfrac{2x+1}{x}$

EXAM TYPE QUESTIONS

Q1

The ancient Babylonian stone tablet shown in Fig. 7.1 gives this formula for the length of the diagonal (d) of a rectangle. The longer side is l and the shorter w. The formula is only an approximation.

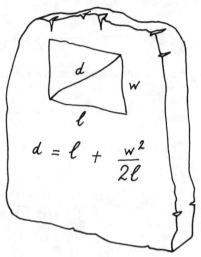

$$d = l + \frac{w^2}{2l}$$

Fig. 7.1

a) What is the difference, to three decimal places, between the correct value of d and that given by the formula, when the rectangle measures i) 6 cm by 5 cm, and ii) 10 cm by 1 cm?

b) Re-arrange the formula to make w the subject.   (MEG; 1988)

Q2

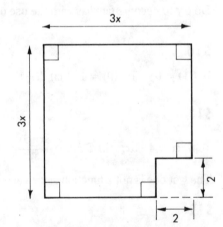

Fig. 7.2

a) Write down, in terms of x, an expression for the area of the shape in Fig. 7.2.

b) Multiply out $(3x + 2)(3x - 2)$, giving your answer in its simplest form.

c) By making one cut and reassembling, the shape in Fig. 7.2 can be made into a rectangle. Using your answers to a) and b), draw a diagram to show how this can be done. Mark the dimensions of the rectangle on your diagram.   (NEA; 1988)

Q3

The cost, £C, of making n articles is given by the formula

   $C = a + bn$.

where a and b are constants. The cost of making 4 articles is £20 and the cost of making 7 articles is £29.

a) Write down two equations in a and b.

b) Solve these equations to find the values of a and b.   (LEAG; 1988)

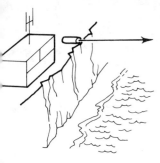

Fig. 7.3

Q4

A rescue harpoon is fired horizontally from a cliff top, as shown in Fig. 7.3. The horizontal distance, x metres, it has travelled after t seconds is given by $x = 250t$. The distance of the harpoon below the cliff top, y metres, is given by $y = 5t^2$.

a) i) Write t in terms of x.
    ii) Write an equation which connects y and x, but does not include t, in the form
        $y = \ldots$
b) How many centimetres below the cliff top will the harpoon be when it is 50 metres horizontally from the firing gun?   (WJEC; 1988)

Q5

$$f(x) = 3 - 2x$$

a) Calculate f(4)
b) Calculate ff(4)
c) Obtain and simplify an expression for ff(x)
d) Calculate $f^{-1}(2)$
e) Obtain an expression for $f^{-1}(x)$ (MEG; 1988)

Q6

Two functions f and g are defined as follows:

$$f(x) = \frac{1}{2x-1} \ (x \neq 0.5) \quad g(x) = x^2$$

a) Find the values of i) f(2);   ii) gf(2)
b) Find an expression for i) gf(x);   ii) fg(x)
c) Show that there is only one value of 'a' for which fg(a) = gf(a)   (NEA; 1988)

Q7

0	1	2	3	4	5	6	7	8	9
10	11	12	13	14	15	16	17	18	19
20	21	22	23	24	25	26	27	28	29
30	31	32	33	34	35	36	37	38	39
40	41	42	43	....					

Fig. 7.4

Look at the number pattern in Fig. 7.4.

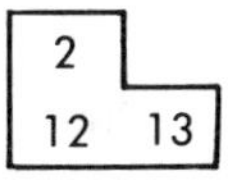

The section in Fig. 7.5 is called the **12L** because **12** is the middle number.

Fig. 7.5

To find the value of 12L you multiply the end numbers and add the middle number, as follows: $(2 \times 13) + 12$. Therefore the value of 12L is 38.

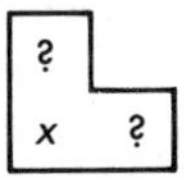

Fig. 7.6

a) What is the value of the 27L section?
b) i) Write down the numbers missing from this L in Fig. 7.6 in terms of x.
    ii) Find the value of this L in terms of x.
c) Which L has a value of 998?   (WJEC; 1988)

Q8

The outer rectangle shown in Fig. 7.7 measures $(2x + 3)$ by $(x + 2)$.

a) Express the area of the shaded rectangle in terms of x.
b) Express the area of the unshaded region in terms of x, in as simplified a form as possible.
c) Calculate the value of x when the area of the shaded region is 2 square units less than the area of the unshaded region.   (NEA; 1988)

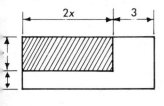

Fig. 7.7

EXTENSION

Q9

Three numbers x, y, z have the property that

$$(y - z) \times (z - x) \times (x - y) = 0.$$

a) From this, **one** of the following statements can be deduced. State which and give a reason for your answer.
    1 At least one of x, y, z is zero.
    2 At least two of x, y, z is zero.
    3 The numbers x, y, z are all zero.
    4 At least two of x, y, z are equal.
    5 The numbers x, y, z are all equal.

b) You are given that three numbers x, y, z satisfy the equations

$$(y - z)(z - x)(x - y) = 0$$
$$\textbf{and} \quad x + 1 = 2y + 3 = 3z + 6.$$

There are three possible sets of values for x, y, z. Find them.   (O and C; 1988)

Q10

The equation $a^2 + b^2 = c^2$ gives the relation between the lengths of the sides of a right angled triangle, c being the length of the hypotenuse and a and b the lengths of the other sides respectively. We wish to find integer values of a, b and c to satisfy the equation.

a) Show that the formulae $a = v^2 - u^2$, $b = 2uv$, and $c = u^2 + v^2$ may be used to find the required values.

b) How must u and v be chosen so that a, b and c have no common factor?   (WJEC; 1988)

Q11

Here are four consecutive numbers 13, 14, 15, 16.
If you multiply the middle pair, you get $14 \times 15 = 210$.
If you multiply the outer pair, you get $13 \times 16 = 208$.
 i) Do a calculation like this for a different set of four consecutive numbers of your own choice.
 ii) Repeat i) twice more. You should notice a general rule. State this clearly in words.
 iii) Use algebra to prove that your rule always works with any four consecutive numbers.
 iv) Find a similar rule which works if you start with four consecutive odd numbers (such as 17, 19, 21, 23). Use algebra to prove this rule.   (O and C; 1988)

Q12

Two trains travel on parallel tracks towards each other at 60 mph and 80 mph respectively. At twelve o'clock they usually pass two points A and B respectively 80 miles apart.

a) Find where the trains pass each other.

b) One day, the slower train was late and passed the express train at a point 6 miles nearer to A than the usual passing point. Assuming the express train to be punctual and both trains to be travelling at the usual speeds, find how many minutes later than usual the slower train was that day.   (WJEC; 1988)

OUTLINE ANSWERS TO EXAM QUESTIONS

A1

a) i) Actual value of $d = \sqrt{(6^2+5^2)} = 7.81025$.

Babylonian formula gives $d = 6+\dfrac{25}{12} = 8.08333$. The difference is 0.273.

ii) Actual value of $d = \sqrt{(10^2+1^2)} = 10.049876$.

Babylonian formula gives $d = 10+\dfrac{1}{20} = 10.05$. The difference is 0.00012379, which to three decimal places is 0.000.

b) From $d = l+\dfrac{w^2}{2l} \to d-l = \dfrac{w^2}{2l} \to 2l(d-l) = w^2$

$\to w = \sqrt{2ld-2l^2}$.

A2

a) $9x^2 - 4$
b) $9x^2 - 4$
c) See Fig. 7.8.

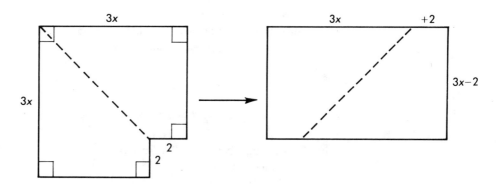

Fig. 7.8

A3

a) $20 = a + 4b$ . . . (1)   and $29 = a + 7b$ . . . (2).
b) Solve the two simultaneous equations to give $b = 3$ and $a = 8$.

A4

a) i) $t = \dfrac{x}{250}$

ii) $y = 5t^2 \to y = 5\left(\dfrac{x}{250}\right)^2 \to y = \dfrac{5x^2}{62500} = \dfrac{x^2}{12500}$

b) When $x = 50, y = \dfrac{50^2}{12500} = 0.2$ metres $= 20$ cm.

A5

a) $f(4) = 3 - 8 = -5$
b) $ff(4) = f(-5) = 3 + 10 = 13$.
c) $ff(x) = f(3 - 2x) = 3 - 2(3 - 2x) = 3 - 6 + 4x = 4x - 3$.
d) $f^{-1}(2) = 0.5$.
e) $f^{-1}(x) = \dfrac{3 - x}{2}$

A6

a) i) $f(2) = \dfrac{1}{3}$;   ii) $gf(2) = g(\tfrac{1}{3}) = \dfrac{1}{9}$

b) i) $gf(x) = g\left(\dfrac{1}{2x-1}\right) = \left(\dfrac{1}{2x-1}\right)^2$

    ii) $fg(x) = f(x^2) = \dfrac{1}{2x^2-1}$

c) When $gf(a) = fg(a)$ then $\dfrac{1}{(2a-1)^2} = \dfrac{1}{2a^2-1}$

$$\rightarrow (2a-1)^2 = 2a^2 - 1$$
$$\rightarrow 4a^2 - 4a + 1 = 2a^2 - 1$$
$$\rightarrow 2a^2 - 4a + 2 = 0 \qquad \rightarrow a^2 - 2a + 1 = 0$$
$$\rightarrow (a-1)^2 = 0$$
$$\rightarrow a = 1$$

There is only the one solution.

A7

a) $(17 \times 28) + 27 = 503.$

b) i) $(x-10)$ and $(x+1).$

    ii) $(x-10)(x+1) + x = x^2 - 9x - 10 + x$
$$= x^2 - 8x - 10.$$

c) When $L = 998$
    then $x^2 - 8x - 10 = 998$
$$\rightarrow \quad x^2 - 8x - 1008 = 0$$
    which will solve to give $x = 36$ and $x = -28.$
    Here we need the positive solution of 36.

A8

a) $2x^2$

b) $(2x + 3)(x + 2) - 2x^2 = 2x^2 + 7x + 6 - 2x^2$
$$= 7x + 6$$

c) This will be when $2x^2 + 2 = 7x + 6.$
    Hence $2x^2 - 7x - 4 = 0.$
    which will solve to give $x = -0.5$ and $x = 4.$
    Here we need the positive solution of $x = 4.$

A9

a) Conditions 1, 2, 3 and 5 are all special cases where the equation is satisfied. Since $(y-z)(z-x)(x-y) = 0$, then all we can deduce is that one of the brackets is zero, hence either $y = z$ **or** $z = x$ **or** $x = y$, hence at least two of x, y, z are equal. Condition 4 is satisfied.

b) There are three possibilities for $(y - z)(z - x)(x - y) = 0.$
    These are that $y = z, z = x$ or $x = y.$
    First, consider $y = z$
      then where $x + 1 = 2y + 3 = 3z + 6$
$$x + 1 = [2y + 3 = 3y + 6]$$
$$[2y+3 = 3y+6] \rightarrow -3 = y$$
    hence $x + 1 = -6 + 3 = -3 \rightarrow x = -4.$
    So $-4, -3, -3$, is a possible solution.
    Next, consider $z = x$
      then where $x + 1 = 2y + 3 = 3z + 6$
$$[x + 1] = 2y + 3 = [3x + 6]$$
$$[x + 1 = 3x + 6] \rightarrow -5 = 2x \rightarrow x = -2.5$$
      hence $-2.5 + 1 = 2y + 3$
$$\rightarrow -4.5 = 2y \rightarrow y = -2.25$$
    So $-2.5, -2.25, -2.5$ is another solution.

Lastly, consider $x = y$

then where $x+1 = 2y+3 = 3z+6$

$$[x+1 = 2x+3] = 3z+6$$

$[x+1 = 2x+3] \rightarrow -2 = x$

hence $-2+1 = 3z+6 \rightarrow z = \dfrac{-7}{3}$

So $-2, -2, \dfrac{-7}{3}$ is the third solution.

The three possible solutions to x, y, z are $(-4, -3, -3)$

$$(-2.5, -2.25, -2.5)$$

$$\left(-2, -2, \frac{-7}{3}\right)$$

A10

a) From $a^2 + b^2 = c^2$, take the left hand side where $a = v^2 - u^2$ and $b = 2uv$

then $a^2 + b^2 = (v^2 - u^2)^2 + (2uv)^2$

$$= v^4 - 2u^2v^2 + u^4 + 4u^2v^2$$

$$= v^4 + 2u^2v^2 + u^4.$$

Take the right hand side where $c = u^2 + v^2$

then $c^2 = (u^2 + v^2)^2 = u^4 + 2u^2v^2 + v^4.$

It can now be seen that $a^2 + b^2 = u^4 + 2u^2v^2 + v^4 = c^2$

$\rightarrow a^2 + b^2 = c^2.$

So the equations do hold on to the validity of $a^2 + b^2 = c^2$. Also, if we choose values of u and v to be integers, then so too will be v^2, u^2 and $2uv$, hence so too will be $v^2 - u^2$, $2uv$ and $v^2 + u^2$. So a, b and c will be integers in value.

b) If a, b and c have a common factor, say x, then when $a = Ax$, $b = Bx$, $c = Cx$, A, B and C are integers and so we will have $Ax = v^2 - u^2$, $Bx = 2uv$, $Cx = u^2 + v^2$.

Hence, since A, B and C are integers then

$$\dfrac{v^2 - u^2}{x}, \dfrac{2uv}{x}, \dfrac{u^2 + v^2}{x} \text{ are also all integers.}$$

Hence $(v^2 - u^2)$, $2uv$ and $(u^2 + v^2)$ are all multiples of x

$\rightarrow$ that both v^2 and u^2 are multiples of x

$\rightarrow$ both v and u are multiples of x.

So if we are to avoid a, b and c having common factors we must choose values of u and v that do not have common factors.

A11

i) You could choose **any** four consecutive numbers, for example, 3, 4, 5, 6 is a simple one to start with, which gives

middle pair $= 4 \times 5 = 20$

outer pair $= 3 \times 6 = 18$

ii) Choose two more sets (no need to choose large numbers, but you can if you wish). The general rule you should find is this – the product of the middle pair is always 2 more than the product of the outer pair.

iii) If we let x be the first number, then the next three after that will be $x + 1, x + 2, x + 3$, to give the consecutive numbers:

$x, x + 1, x + 2, x + 3.$

The product of the middle pair $= (x + 1)(x + 2) = x^2 + 3x + 2.$

The product of the outer pair $= x(x + 3) \qquad = x^2 + 3x.$

The difference is $(x^2 + 3x + 2) - (x^2 + 3x) = 2.$

So for all x, the difference is still 2.

iv) Let x be the first odd number, then the four consecutive odd numbers will be:

$x, x + 2, x + 4, x + 6.$

The product of the middle pair $= (x + 2)(x + 4) = x^2 + 6x + 8.$

The product of the outer pair $= x(x + 6) \qquad = x^2 + 6x.$

So the difference is 8, giving the rule that 'the product of the middle pair of consecutive odd numbers is 8 more than the product of the outer pair.'

P.S. This also works for consecutive even numbers.

A12

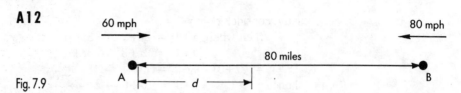

60 mph   80 mph

80 miles

A   d   B

Fig. 7.9

a) In Fig. 7.9 let distance, d, be the point where the trains pass. Then t = time travelled in hours. The slower train will satisfy the equation $d = 60t$, while the faster train will satisfy the equation $d = 80 - 80t$.

So if d is when they pass, then $60t = 80 - 80t$

$$\rightarrow 140t = 80 \quad \rightarrow t = 0.5714 \text{ hours}$$

gives the time on passing at 34 minutes and the distance from A given by 60×0.5714 = 34.3 miles.

b) If the trains passed 6 miles nearer to A, then they passed at a distance of 28.3 miles from A. As the express train was punctual, to find out how long it took that train to cover a distance of $(80 - 28.3)$ miles, we evaluate

$$\text{time} = \frac{\text{distance}}{\text{speed}} = \frac{51.7}{80} = 0.64625 \text{ hours} = 38.8 \text{ minutes.}$$

The slower train took $\dfrac{28.3}{60} = 0.4667 = 28$ minutes to reach that point. The difference in time tells how late the first train was, which was 10.8, rounded off to 11 minutes late.

A STUDENT'S ANSWER
WITH EXAMINER'S COMMENTS

Question

A road tanker carries 30 tonnes of oil. When cold, the oil can be pumped out at a rate of x tonnes per minute.

a) Write down an expression for the time, in minutes, taken to empty the tanker.

> **" Good, clear and correct answers. "**

Answer $\dfrac{30}{x}$

If the oil is heated then an extra 0.5 tonnes can be pumped out per minute.

b) Write down an expression for the time taken to empty the tanker when the oil is heated.

Answer $\dfrac{30}{x + 0.5}$

> **" Could have been better laid out, but it is correct and we can see what you have done. "**

If the oil has been heated then the time taken to empty the tanker is reduced by two minutes.

c) Show that the equation for x can be expressed in the form

$$2x^2 + x - 15 = 0$$

> **" Good to see how you are trying to solve the equation. "**

$$\frac{30}{x} - \frac{30}{x + 0.5} = 2 \qquad \frac{30(x + 0.5) - 30x}{x(x + 0.5)} = 2$$

$$30x + 15 - 30x = 2x^2 + x$$

$$15 = 2x^2 + x \quad \text{So } 2x^2 + x - 15 = 0$$

Solve this equation for x, and hence find the time taken to empty the tanker when the oil is cold.

> **" Correct final answer, but no mention has been made of *why* the negative answer of $x = -3$ has been rejected. This would lose a mark. "**

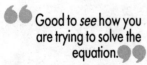

$$(2x - 5)(x + 3) = 0$$

$$\text{So } x = 2.5 \text{ and } -3$$

Answer $x = 2.5$

A good answer showing algebraic manipulation has been clearly understood. You will get high marks for this answer.

CHAPTER 8

GRAPHS

DRAWING GRAPHS FROM EQUATIONS

GRAPHS AND THEIR 'STORIES'

GRAPHS OF INEQUALITIES

G E T T I N G   S T A R T E D

For the highest grades of GCSE you must be able to draw a good graph from any of the equations given, and to recognise the type of equation a given graph will have. You will be expected to sort out your own sensible scales and to draw your graphs with accuracy. The accuracy needed in examinations is usually to the nearest millimetre.

Graphs will generally be drawn in order to find an algebraic solution, or a gradient or an area beneath the graph. Sometimes a graph will be drawn as an end in itself.

USEFUL DEFINITIONS

Cubic
A cubic equation is one which has a cube as the highest power, e.g. $y^3 + 6y^2 + y = 5$.

Gradient
The 'steepness' of a line. It is the tangent of the angle made with the horizontal.

Intercept
Where a line crosses an axis.

Linear
A linear *equation* is one which involves only single variables of power one, e.g. $2x + y = 5$. A linear *graph* will be a straight line.

Quadratic
A quadratic *equation* is one which has a square as the highest power, e.g $2x^2 + 4x = 3$.
A quadratic *curve* is the graph of a quadratic equation and it is a symmetrical **U** shape.

ESSENTIAL PRINCIPLES

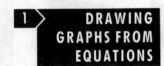

There are four main types of equation for which you should be able to draw graphs.

LINEAR EQUATIONS

A *linear equation* is of the form $y = mx + c$ where m and c are constants. This will always give a straight line, and the minimum number of points to plot is three. The easiest way to sketch or draw this type of equation is to find the x and y intercepts and one other point. Then draw the straight line that goes through all these points.

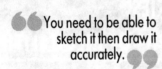

Sketch the graph of $5x + 2y = 7$.

Find the x axis intercept by substituting $y = 0$, which gives $5x = 7$, $x = 1.4$. So one point is found as $(1.4, 0)$. Find the y axis intercept by substituting $x = 0$, which gives $2y = 7$; $y = 3.5$. So another point is found as $(0, 3.5)$. Find another by substituting, say, $y = 2$, which gives $5x + 4 = 7 \rightarrow 5x = 3 \rightarrow x = 0.6$, hence the third point is found as $(0.6, 2)$. These can now be plotted and a straight line drawn through them, as shown in Fig. 8.1.

> You need to be able to sketch it then draw it accurately.

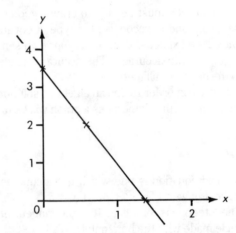

Fig. 8.1

EXERCISE 1

Sketch the graphs of $x + y = 8$ and $2x - y = 3$, stating the co-ordinate of intersection.

QUADRATIC EQUATIONS

A *quadratic equation* is of the form $y = ax^2 + bx + c$, where a, b and c are constants. This will always give you a curved graph, and the interesting part usually asked for is this part that does a U turn. See the two possible shapes in Fig 8.2:

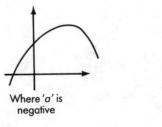

Where 'a' is negative

Where 'a' is positive

Fig. 8.2

You will need quite a few points plotting, especially round the 'dip' or 'hill top'. In an examination it is most likely that you will be told the range of values to plot and hence the 'dip' will be among that range if the question requires it.

The main use of the 'dip' is to tell you the least possible value that the function has, or if it is the 'top of a hill' then the greatest possible value the function has.

Neil, a bit of a mathematician, reckoned that when he played golf and teed off with a 'one iron' then the path of the ball was given by the following equation: $y = \dfrac{3x(95 - x)}{200}$ where y is the vertical distance above the tee and x is the horizontal distance from the tee. With a 'one iron', Neil usually managed to hit the ball about 100 metres. Draw a graph of the path of the ball and find out its greatest height.

A table needs to be built up of values of x from 0 to 100. If we start with x going up in 20s to start with, we get the table in Fig. 8.3.

x	0	20	40	60	80	100
$3x$	0	60	120	180	240	300
$95-x$	95	75	55	35	15	-5
$y = \dfrac{3x(95-x)}{200}$	0	22.5	33	31.5	18	-7.5

Fig. 8.3

This now lets us plot the points as in Fig. 8.4.

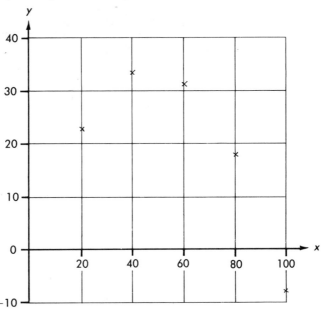

Fig. 8.4

> ❝❝ Notice that I chose a scale that will fit the points on but not be too big. ❞❞

We could do with finding a few more points near the top of the hill. This seems around $x = 50$. Hence, find the y ordinate at $x = 42$, 45 and 48. Evaluating these gives us (42, 33.4), (45, 33.75), (50, 33.75). When we plot these points we get a much better picture of the solution and can now draw the graph as in Fig. 8.5, and the maximum height can be seen to be *33.8 metres*.

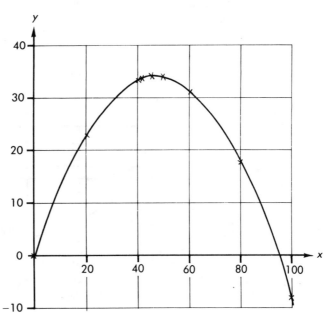

Fig. 8.5

EXERCISE 2

Draw the graph of $y = x^2 + 3x + 4$ and find the least possible value of y. (Use values of x where $-3 \leqslant x \leqslant 1$.)

Solutions to quadratic equations

These can be made from their graphs. For example, the solutions of $ax^2 + bx + c = 0$ will be where the graph of $y = ax^2 + bx + c$ cuts the x axis (i.e., where $y = 0$).

In general, the solution of $ax^2 + bx + c = d$ is where the graph of $y = ax^2 + bx + c$ cuts the line $y = d$.

WORKED EXAMPLE 3

Draw the graph of $y = x^2 + x - 4$ where $-3 \leqslant x \leqslant 3$ and hence find the solution to the equation $x^2 + x = 5$.

Construct the table of values for $-3 \leqslant x \leqslant 3$ as in Fig. 8.6.

x	-3	-2	-1	0	1	2	3
x^2	9	4	1	0	1	4	9
-4	-4	-4	-4	-4	-4	-4	-4
$y = x^2 + x - 4$	2	-2	-4	-4	-2	2	8

Fig. 8.6

This will give you the **U**-shaped curve as in Fig. 8.7.

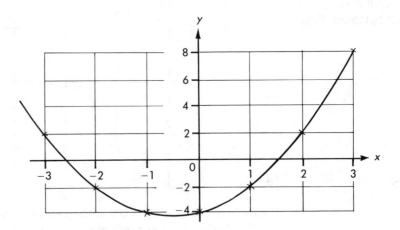

Fig. 8.7

The solution to $x^2 + x = 5$ is given by $x^2 + x - 4 = 1$. (Check that this is the same equation.) Hence where the graph of $y = x^2 + x - 4$ crosses $y = 1$, as in Fig. 8.8. The solutions are where $x = -2.8$ and $x = 1.8$.

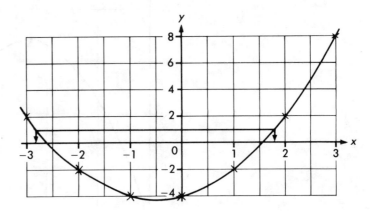

Fig. 8.8

RECIPROCAL EQUATIONS

A reciprocal equation is of the form $y = \dfrac{A}{x}$ where A can be any constant value not equal to zero. This will give a curved shape that has symmetry about the origin as you will see in the worked example.

WORKED EXAMPLE 4

Draw the graph of $y = \dfrac{6}{x}$ between $x = -3$ and $x = 3$ and fully describe all its symmetry.

First, construct the table of values for $-3 \leqslant x \leqslant 3$ as in Fig. 8.9. These points can now be plotted, as in Fig. 8.10. There are two symmetries of the drawn graph, for it has a line symmetry $y = -x$ and rotational symmetry of order 2. (If I had made the scale identical on both axes then $y = x$ would be another line of symmetry.)

Fig. 8.9

x	-3	-2	-1	0	1	2	3
$y = \dfrac{6}{x}$	-2	-3	-6	∞	6	3	2

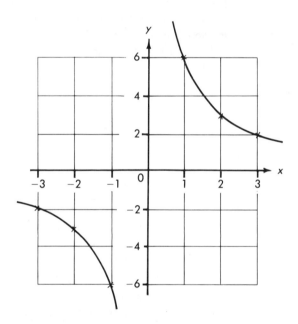

Fig. 8.10

EXERCISE 3

Draw the graphs of $y = \dfrac{12}{x}$ and $y = x^2 - 2x + 1$ where $0 < x < 5$, and so state a solution of the equation $x^3 - 2x^2 + x = 12$.

SIMULTANEOUS EQUATIONS

This last exercise had you solving a simultaneous equation by graph, by simply drawing the graph of each equation and then finding where both graphs cross. This can be a useful way of finding an approximate solution (especially if you need to find an approximate value for starting an *iterative solution*, which we looked at in Chapter 5). However, in general terms, it is always better to try and solve simultaneous equations by an algebraic method rather than by graph if you can, unless an examination question specifically says 'by graph'.

2 ▷ GRAPHS AND THEIR 'STORIES'

The gradients of graphs and the area underneath them can have special meanings for particular graphs. You need to be fully aware of these.

GRADIENTS ON STRAIGHT LINES

We will consider the *gradients of straight lines* first, then look at curves. The gradient of a *straight line* is a number and if the axes have any units on them, then the gradient will take its *units* from those two axes. The *number* for the gradient is found by taking two convenient points on the line as far apart as possible (but keeping the co-ordinates as round numbers if possible). If we say that the first point has co-ordinates (x_1, y_1) and the second point has co-ordinates (x_2, y_2), then the gradient will be equal to $\dfrac{y_2 - y_1}{x_2 - x_1}$, as shown in Fig. 8.11.

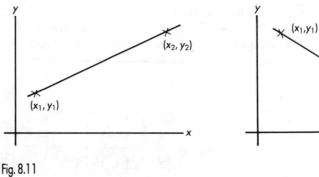

Fig. 8.11

Making sure your x_2 is always the biggest of the x co-ordinates will give you a *positive* denominator, so that when $y_2 > y$, your gradient is positive (uphill) and when $y_2 < y$, the gradient is negative (downhill).

Look through the examples of axes, lines and gradients shown in Fig. 8.12 to gain the feel for changing axis units to gradient units.

> **These practical situations need understanding and remembering, they will be asked in the exam.**

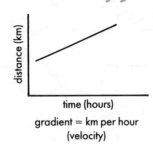

gradient = km per hour
(velocity)

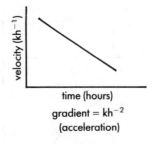

gradient = kh^{-2}
(acceleration)

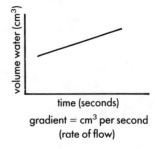

gradient = cm^3 per second
(rate of flow)

Fig. 8.12

The first two examples in Fig. 8.12 are the most common ones that you will meet in the examination, where the gradient of a time, distance graph is always the *velocity*, and the gradient of a time, velocity graph is always the *acceleration*.

If you have the equation of the straight line, which can always be put into the form of $y = mx + c$ where m and c are some constants, then the *coefficient of x*, namely m, will always be equal to the *gradient* of the graph of that equation.

EXERCISE 4

The graph in Fig. 8.13 illustrates how Malcolm's speed changed on the motorway one morning. What was his acceleration at   i) 8.15;   ii) 8.30;   iii) 8.45?

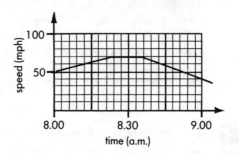

Fig. 8.13

GRADIENTS ON CURVES

The *gradient on a curve* keeps changing! That is why the graph *is* a curve and not a straight line! So, to find the gradient on a curve you have to draw the straight line that *just* touches the curve at that point (the *tangent* to the curve at that point). Then the gradient of the curve at that point is the same as the gradient of that straight line.

WORKED EXAMPLE 5

The graph in Fig. 8.14 illustrates how Helen had swum in a 100 m freestyle race. Find her velocity after   i) 5 seconds;   ii) 15 seconds.

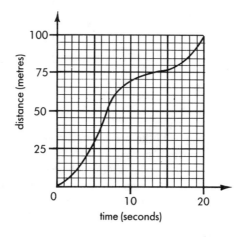

Fig. 8.14

> The tangent is a line that just touches the curve at that point and not cross it. But it may well cross the curve further on as the two examples here both show.

We need to draw the tangent to the curve at each point and find its gradient.
i) In Fig 8.15, after 5 seconds we see that the gradient of the tangent at the curve is given by $\frac{65m}{8s} = 8.1\text{ms}^{-1}$.

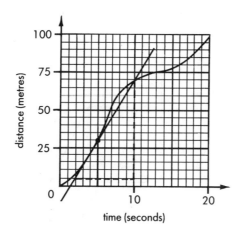

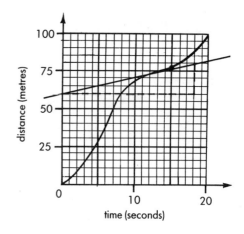

Fig. 8.15   Fig. 8.16

ii) In Fig. 8.16, after 15 seconds the tangent to the curve does cut the curve later on but at the point, 15 seconds, it is touching the curve and *not* cutting through it. Here the gradient of the tangent is given by $\frac{20m}{18s} = 1.1\text{ms}^{-1}$.

EXERCISE 5

The velocity, v ms^{-1} of a ball after a time, t sec, over the first 4 seconds, is given by the equation $v = 4t - t^2$.
i) find the acceleration of the ball after 3 seconds, and
ii) what is the greatest velocity of the ball, and what is its acceleration at that time?

AREAS UNDER GRAPHS

Straight line graphs

Consider first the area under a *straight line graph*. Work through the following two examples:

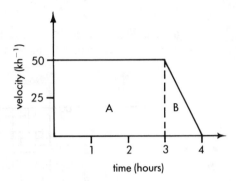

Fig. 8.17

WORKED EXAMPLE 6

In Fig. 8.17 the horizontal line indicates a steady speed of 50 km per hour for 3 hours. This will cover a distance of $50 \times 3 = 150$ km. The area, A, under this line is also 50×3 (using the units on the scale), indicating that the area under the graph on a velocity/time graph indicates the distance travelled. Now, consider the area B under the line, which indicates the velocity dropping steadily from 50 km per hour to a standstill. The area underneath is the area of the triangle $\frac{1}{2} \times 1 \times 50 = 25$ km. Hence the total distance covered here will be $150 + 25 = 175$ km.

WORKED EXAMPLE 7

In Fig. 8.18 the graph indicates the water flow through a pipe, steadily for the first 20 minutes then slowing down to nothing after 30 minutes. The horizontal line indicates the steady flow of 40 litres per minute for 20 minutes, which will be a total flow of $40 \times 20 = 800$ litres, also found by the corresponding area A under the line. Similarly the area B under the sloping graph indicates the amount of water flowing through the pipe over the last 10 minutes, which is $\frac{1}{2} \times 10 \times 40 = 200$ litres. So the total volume of water that flowed through the pipe was $800 + 200 = 1000$ litres.

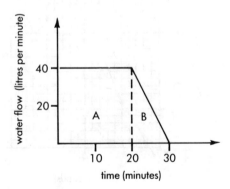

Fig. 8.18

Area under curves

The previous idea is continued under *curves*, where the area will represent some quantity defined by the axes. The problem with curves of course is calculating the area. There are two common methods; one is *counting squares* to approximate the area, (although strictly speaking we do not have to use squares and in practice rectangles are very often used just as effectively) and another is *splitting the shape up into estimated trapeziums* and calculating the area of each to give us an estimated total. (The most accurate way is with *calculus* and you will discover this neat way when you study for your A level.)

Counting squares

The graph in Fig. 8.19 indicates the speed of Kirsty while jogging round a sponsored run. To estimate the total distance Kirsty covered, count the number of squares under the

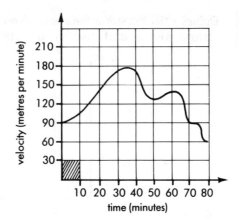

Fig. 8.19

curve. This, I estimate as 34 squares. Now consider one square. Look at the bottom left hand square next to the origin. This represents 30 m per minute for 10 minutes, which is a distance of $30 \times 10 = 300$ metres. Hence the total distance Kirsty covered was 34×300 metres = 10200 metres, which is 10.2 km.

It is very important to find what the area of each square actually stands for, and the one at the bottom left hand corner next to the origin is usually the easiest one to help you to work this out.

Trapezoidal method
This is useful where there are perhaps too many reasonable squares to count and you want an easier rule of thumb method. Follow the example in Fig. 8.20 to show you how this method can work quite effectively.

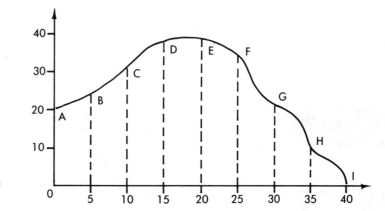

Fig. 8.20

The area of a trapezium is found by the average of the lengths of the two parallel sides divided by the distance between them. So in the above shape, split into eight trapeziums, where the length of the parallel sides (the vertical sides) are of lengths A, B, C . . . . I respectively, and all a distance of 5 from each other, the total area would be found by:

$$\text{Area} = \frac{5(A + B)}{2} + \frac{5(B + C)}{2} + \frac{5(C + D)}{2} \cdots + \frac{5(G + H)}{2} + \frac{5(H + I)}{2}$$

$$= \frac{5}{2}\left[(A+B) + (B+C) + (C+D) + \cdots + (G+H) + (H+I) \right]$$

Total area $= \frac{5}{2} \{A + 2(B+C+D+E+F+G+H) + I\}$

This gives us a good rule of thumb to work with to estimate the area under the curve, i.e.

i)   Split into as many strips as you wish, width of each, d.
ii)   Add up first and last length.
iii) Add up all those in between and double.
iv)   Add these last two together.
v)   Now multiply by d and halve.
vi)   You have your estimated total area!

WORKED EXAMPLE 8

During a thunderstorm the rainfall down a particular road was measured and graphed as illustrated in Fig. 8.21. Estimate the total rainwater that flowed down the road that day.

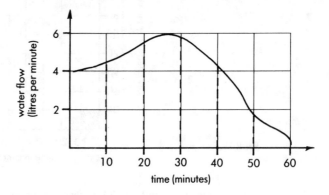

Fig. 8.21

Draw on the diagram strips to form the parallel sides of the trapeziums.
The width of each strip is 10.
The end lengths are 4 and 0, giving a total of 4.
The middle lengths add up to $4.4 + 5.4 + 5.8 + 4.4 + 1.6 = 21.6$, which when doubled and added to 4 gives $(21.6 \times 2) + 4 = 47.2$.
Multiply this by 10, divide by 2, to give 236
i.e. total $= \dfrac{10}{2} \{4 + 2(4.4 + 5.4 + 5.8 + 4.4 + 1.6) + 0\} = 236$

The unit *square* we have been using is 1 litre per minute $\times$ 1 minute $=$ 1 litre. Hence the total water flow would be 236 litres.

EXERCISE 6

Gillian, who was learning to drive, was practising by driving along quiet country lanes. Over the first 4 hours she drove with a speed v kilometres per hour, varying with time, t hours, given by the equation $v = t^3 - 4t^2 + 3t + 20$.
Find the total distance covered in these 4 hours.

3 ▷ GRAPHS OF INEQUALITIES

The only type of inequalities that you are likely to be considering are linear inequalities like $y > x$ or $y > 3x + 2$ or $x < 5$. These are all either one side or another of a straight line, and to find this region, again there is a simple set of rules to follow:

WORKED EXAMPLE 9

To draw the graph of the inequality $y > mx + c$.
i) Draw the line with equation $y = mx + c$.
ii) Choose any point either side of that line, say (1,2), then when you substitute this point into the inequality, either the statement is now true or false; if true shade in the side containing that point, if false, then shade in the other side.

WORKED EXAMPLE 10

Draw the graph of $y > 4x - 3$.
i) Draw the graph of $y = 4x - 3$, as shown in Fig. 8.22.

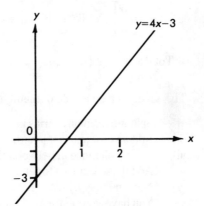

Fig. 8.22

ii) Choose a convenient point, say, the origin (0,0). Substitute this into the inequality $y > 4x-3$, which is true, hence the side containing (0,0) is the one that needs shading in Fig. 8.23.

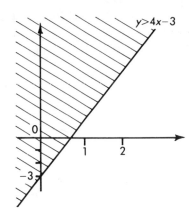

Fig. 8.23

EXERCISE 7

Sketch the graph of $x + y < 1$.

SOLUTION SETS

The use of graphing inequalities (or inequations as they are sometimes called) is to find *solution sets* to a particular problem. This is often called 'linear programming', where you usually have to find two (or more) inequalities, graph them and find which possible solutions satisfy both situations. To do this most effectively you are advised to shade out the regions you do not want so that you are left with the region you do want.

WORKED EXAMPLE 11

The Carterknowle housing development wish to buy 5600 m² of land on which they intend to build x houses and y bungalows.

a) Each house uses 400 m² of land and each bungalow uses 700 m² of land. Write down an inequality between x and y.
b) A house cost £84 000 to build and a bungalow cost £60 000 to build. £840 000 has been set aside for building costs. Write down and simplify an equation for this.
c) Represent these inequalities graphically.
d) Research shows that the developer can make a profit of £18 000 on a house and £15 000 on a bungalow. How many of each type of building should he build to obtain the maximum profit. What is this profit?

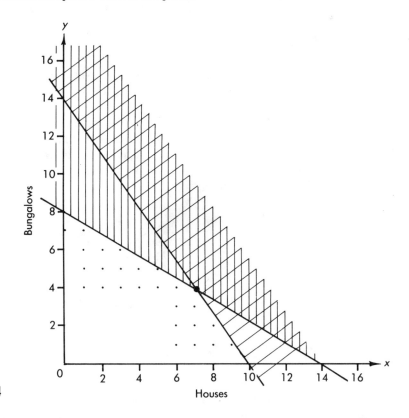

Fig. 8.24

a) From the original question we can say that $400x + 700y \leqslant 5600$. This will simplify to $4x + 7y \leqslant 56$.

b) This will be $84\ 000x + 60\ 000y \leqslant 840\ 000$, which will simplify to $84x + 60y \leqslant 840$, which simplifies even further to $7x + 5y \leqslant 70$.

c) The graph should look like that in Fig. 8.24, the unshaded area representing the possible solution set. The dots represent the actual possible solutions. Care needs to be taken to identify those points possible on or near to the lines.

d) Profit $\propto (18\ 000x + 15\ 000y) \rightarrow$ Profit $\propto (18x + 15y)$
$$\rightarrow \text{Profit} \propto (6x + 5y).$$

So we need to draw a line Profit $= 6x + 5y$ and find where this maximum point is. In Fig. 8.25, the dashed line shows the graph of $6x + 5y = 30$, so the maximum Profit $= 6x + 5y$ is parallel to this and the one that will be furthest out from the origin.

> **"** Your choice of scale is critical here, since your graph needs to be as large as possible to be accurate as possible. **"**

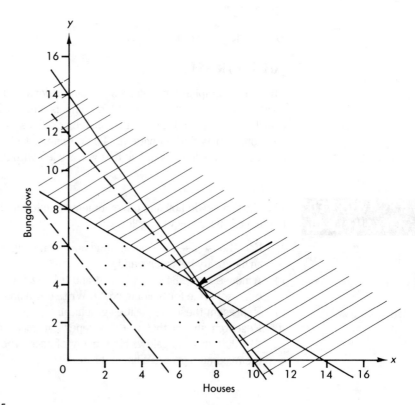

Fig. 8.25

The arrow shows this maximum point found on the line where $x = 7$ and $y = 4$. So the maximum profit is $(£18\ 000 \times 7) + (£15\ 000 \times 4) = £186\ 000$. This is building 7 houses and 4 bungalows.

NB. You must always be aware of the inequality sign you are working with, is it $<$ or $\leqslant$, i.e. 'less than' or 'less than or equal to'. Many marks are lost in examinations because students give an answer right on the line where $\leqslant$ holds yet the line is really $<$ (or vice versa). So when you get to your final answer, do check it out, see that it fits the inequality you are working to.

SOLUTIONS TO EXERCISES

S1

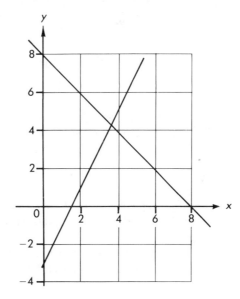

Fig. 8.26

The point of intersection is the point (3.7, 4.3), as shown in Fig. 8.26.

S2

You should have a table of values and a graph, as shown in Fig. 8.27.

x	-3	-2	-1	0	1
x^2	9	4	1	0	1
$3x$	-9	-6	-3	0	3
4	4	4	4	4	4
$y=x^2+3x+4$	4	2	2	4	8

Fig. 8.27

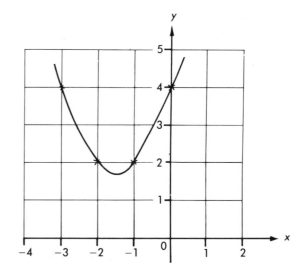

The 'dip' looks to be about $x = -1.5$. We can then find this value substituted into $y = x^2 + 3x + 4$ to get $y = 1.75$, which seems to be confirmed by the graph. So the least possible value of y is 1.75.

S3

You should have tables as shown in Fig. 8.28.

x	1	2	3	4	5
$y=\dfrac{12}{x}$	12	6	4	3	2.4

x	0	1	2	3	4	5
x^2	0	1	4	9	16	25
$-2x$	0	-2	-4	-6	-8	-10
1	1	1	1	1	1	1
$y=x^2-2x+1$	1	0	1	4	9	16

Fig. 8.28

You should then see which 'gaps' needed filling in. These would be chiefly on the $y = x^2 - 2x + 1$ graph around the dip, at $x = \frac{1}{2}$ and $x = 1\frac{1}{2}$. The solution of the equation $x^3 - 2x^2 + x = 12$ is given by the intersection of the two curves as from

$$y = \frac{12}{x} = x^2 - 2x + 1 \rightarrow 12 = x^3 - 2x^2 + x.$$

This point of intersection is at the point $x = 3$ (which you can see from the tables).

S4

i) Gradient of the line gives $57\ \text{mh}^{-2}$.
ii) Gradient of the line is zero, hence no acceleration.
iii) Gradient is negative, indicating deceleration of $75\ \text{mh}^{-2}$ (or acceleration of $-75\ \text{mh}^{-2}$).

S5

Draw the graph of $v = 4t - t^2$, as in Fig. 8.29.
i) Find the gradient at $t = 3$; this will mean drawing the tangent to the curve at that point giving a gradient of $-2\ \text{ms}^{-2}$.
ii) The largest the velocity can get up to is the top of the hill which is where velocity is $4\ \text{ms}^{-2}$. The acceleration at this point is the gradient of the tangent which is zero.

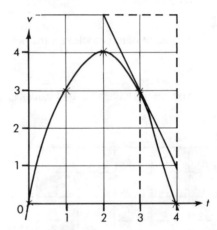

Fig. 8.29

S6

You need to draw the graph then find the area underneath. You should end up with a table of values as in Fig. 8.30.

Fig. 8.30

t	0	1	2	3	4
v	20	20	18	20	32

As you see, you would really need to know what value v has when $t = \frac{1}{2}$. This is $v = 20.625$. The graph can now be drawn as in Fig. 8.31, and can be split into the four strips as shown. Using the trapezium rule we would end up with:

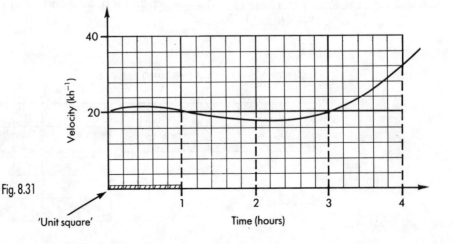

Fig. 8.31

'Unit square'

total area = ½{20 + 2(20 + 18 + 20) + 32} = 84.

The unit 'square' has been 1 kh⁻¹ for 1 hour, which is a distance of 1 kilometre. So the total distance covered by Gillian while practising her driving would be 84 kilometres.

S7

Sketch the line $x + y = 1$ first, as in Fig. 8.32. Then look at a point to one side of the line, say (0,0) and see if this point fits the inequality; $0 + 0 < 1$ is true, so the side that contains this point (0,0) is the region indicated. (Make sure you do show shading in all *four* quadrants.)

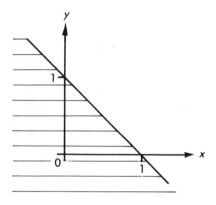

Fig. 8.32

EXAM TYPE QUESTIONS

HIGHER LEVEL

Q1

Given that $3x + 4y + 7 = 0$
i)   Write this equation in the form $y = mx + c$.
ii) What is the gradient of the straight line represented by this equation?   (NEA; 1988)

Q2

Huw observes a bird flying directly away from a bird box. He starts his watch and finds out how far the bird is from the box at different times.

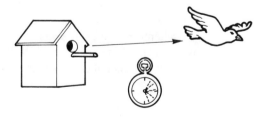

The graph shown in Fig 8.34 was drawn from his results.
a)   How far is the bird from the box when Huw starts his watch?
b)   How fast is the bird flying?
c)   Write down a formula for the distance, d, the bird is from the box in terms of time, t.

(WJEC; 1988)

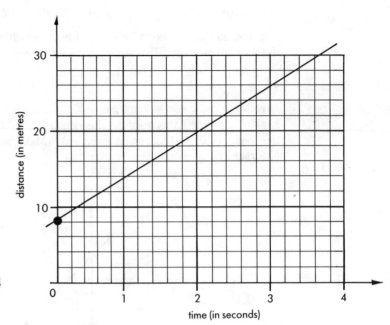

Fig. 8.34

Q3

A school inspector uses his own car to visit schools. He can claim travel expenses each week on one or other of two schemes.

Scheme A: For distances up to 100 miles, 40 pence per mile. For distances over 100 miles, 40 pence per mile for the first 100 miles then 10 pence per mile for each mile after the first 100 miles.

Scheme B: A basic allowance of £10 plus 20 pence per mile travelled.

a)   Copy and complete the table for scheme A: shown in Fig. 8.35.

Miles travelled (x)	0	50	100	150	200	250	300	350	400
Expenses claimed (£y)	0		40		50			65	

Fig. 8.35

b)   On graph paper, using scales of 2 cm to 50 miles travelled and 2 cm to £10 expenses claimed, draw a graph for scheme A for distances travelled up to 400 miles in one week.

c)   On the same axes, draw a graph for scheme B for distances travelled up to 400 miles in one week.

d)   i) Use your graphs to find the two values of x (miles travelled) for which scheme A and scheme B produce equal values of £y (expenses claimed).

   ii) For what range of values of x (miles travelled) does scheme A produce the greater value of £y (expenses claimed)?

   iii) When the distance travelled is 400 miles, find how much more can be claimed using scheme B than using scheme A.

   iv) Find the values of x for which the amount claimed using one scheme is £10 more than the amount claimed using the other scheme.   (LEAG; 1988)

Q4

On the grid in Fig. 8.36, indicate, by the shading out of the region not required, the solution of the inequality $2x + 3y \geqslant 6$.   (MEG; 1988)

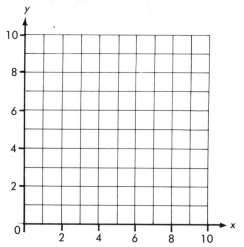

Fig. 8.36

Q5

The values in Fig. 8.37 are based on the performance figures for a Datsun Bluebird car as it accelerates from rest.

Fig. 8.37

Time (seconds), t	0	2	4	6	8	10
velocity (metres per second), v	0	10	18	23.5	27.5	31

a)   Draw the graph of v against t.

b)   By drawing the tangent to the curve at (4, 18), estimate the gradient of the curve at this point, and state the significance of this value.

c)   Estimate the area of the region bounded by the curve, the t-axis and the line $t = 10$ by approximating this area to a triangle and four trapezia. State the significance of this value.   (NEA; 1988)

Q6

The graph in Fig. 8.38 is of $y = x^2 - 2x - 5$.

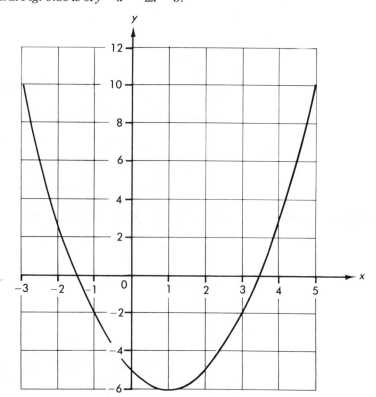

Fig. 8.38

a) Using the same axes, draw the line whose equation is $y = x - 1$.
b) Write down the solution set to $x^2 - 2x - 5 = x - 1$.
c) Show that $x^2 - 2x - 5 = x - 1$ can be written as $x^2 - 3x - 4 = 0$.
d) By drawing a suitable line, using the same axes, solve the equation $x^2 - x - 11 = 0$.

(WJEC; 1988)

Q7

A pebble is thrown upwards from the edge of a seaside cliff and eventually falls into the sea. The height of the pebble above the sea after t seconds is h metres, where h is given by the formula $h = 24 + 8t - 2t^2$.

t	0	1	2	3	4	5	6
h							

Fig. 8.39

a) Copy and complete the table in Fig. 8.39 for the values of h.
b) Using a scale of 2 cm for 5 m on the h-axis and 2 cm for 1 second on the t-axis, draw a graph of h against t for $0 \leqslant t \leqslant 6$.
c) Find i) the height of the cliff; ii) how high the pebble rises above the level of the cliff-top; iii) after how many seconds the pebble lands in the sea; iv) by drawing a suitable line, an estimate for the speed of the pebble after 5 seconds. (LEAG; 1988)

Q8

A rectangular block shown in Fig. 8.40 has a square base of side x cm and a height of h cm. The total surface area of the block is 72 cm^2.

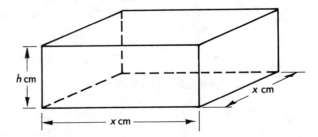

Fig. 8.40

a) Express h in terms of x.
b) Show that the volume, V cm^3, of the block is given by $V = 18x - \dfrac{x^3}{2}$.

c) Copy and complete the table in Fig. 8.41 to show corresponding values of x and V.

x	0	1	2	3	4	5	6
V	0			40.5	40		0

Fig. 8.41

> **Use the scale they've given you or you will lose marks.**

d) Using a scale of 2 cm to represent 1 unit on the x-axis and 2 cm to represent 10 units on the V-axis, draw the graph of $V = 18x - \dfrac{x^3}{2}$ for values of x from 0 to 6 inclusive.

e) A block of this type has a volume of 30 cm^3. Given that $h > x$, find the dimensions of the block.

(MEG; 1988)

Q9

The number of bacteria in a colony doubles every 30 minutes.
a) Complete the table in Fig. 8.42 to show the number of bacteria for the first four hours. The colony starts with 25 bacteria.

Time (hours)	0	½	1	1½	2	2½	3	3½	4
No. of bacteria	25	50							

Fig. 8.42

b) i) Draw a graph to represent these figures, forming the points with a smooth curve.
    ii) From the graph find the time when there will be 2500 bacteria.
c) If the number continues to double every 30 minutes, calculate how many bacteria there would be after 10 hours.   (MEG; 1988)

Q10

EXTENSION

a) An open-air swimming pool is filled through a pipe. The rate of flow is 10 000 litres per hour from noon until 7 pm, and it is increased to 15 000 litres per hour from 7 pm until 9 pm. This is shown on the graph in Fig. 8.43.

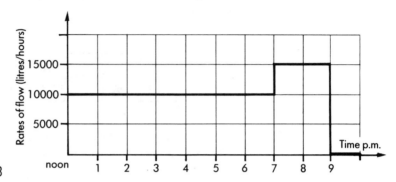

Fig. 8.43

Show that the total amount of water put into the pool is measured by the area under the graph.

b) At midnight it starts to rain. The graph in Fig. 8.44 shows the rate at which the rain falls on the pool.

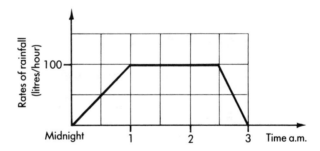

Fig. 8.44

    i) Describe in words how the rainfall varies between midnight and 3 am.
    ii) Assuming that the total amount of rain that falls on the pool is measured by the area under the graph, calculate this amount in litres.
    iii) When the pool was filled through the pipe the previous day, the average depth of the water was 2 metres. How much does the water level rise as a result of the rain?
c) Between 8 am and 9 am there is a thunderstorm. The graph in Fig. 8.45 shows the rate at which rain falls on the pool during the storm.

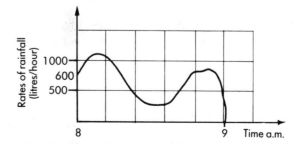

Fig. 8.45

Use an approximate method to estimate how much rain falls on the pool during the storm.   (O and C; 1988)

Q11

John is trying to design a more efficient speedboat. He has designed the hull of the boat and tested it. He recorded the drag d (the resistance of the water), measured in Newtons at various velocities (V).

Velocity, V (m/s)	0.50	1.00	1.50	2.00	2.50	3.00
Drag d (Newtons)	0.52	1.15	2.41	4.07	5.88	8.53

Fig. 8.46

a) Explain how John can tell from the table of values in Fig. 8.46 that the graph of (V,d) is not a straight line.

b) He wanted to test whether the drag would satisfy a formula of the type $d = aV^2 + b$ where a and b are constants. He made a new table to show the values of V^2 and d. Complete the new table in Fig. 8.47 to show the values of V^2 and d obtained from the table above.

V^2	0.25	1.00				
d	0.52	1.15	2.41	4.07	5.88	8.53

Fig. 8.47

c) i) When John graphed this table, why do you think he would be satisfied?
   ii) Deduce the formula that John is likely to declare satisfies the performance of his speedboat.

OUTLINE ANSWERS TO EXAM QUESTIONS

A1

a) $3x + 4y + 7 = 0 \rightarrow 4y = -3x - 7$
$$\rightarrow y = -\frac{3}{4}x - \frac{7}{4}$$

b) The gradient is the co-efficient of x which is $-\dfrac{3}{4}$

A2

a) 8 metres. (It is the point on the graph where $t = 0$.)

b) The gradient of the line which is found from two points (0,8) and (3,26) to give
$$\frac{26 - 8}{3 - 0} = \frac{18}{3} = 6 \text{ ms}^{-1}$$

c) The equation is of the form $y = mx + c$ where m is the gradient and c the y-axis intercept. So here it will be $d = 6t + 8$.

A3

a) See Fig. 8.48.

Miles travelled (x)	0	50	100	150	200	250	300	350	400
Expenses claimed (£y)	0	20	40	45	50	55	60	65	70

Fig. 8.48

b)   See Fig. 8.49.

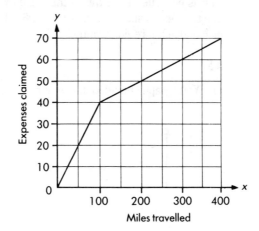

Fig. 8.49

c)   See Fig. 8.50.

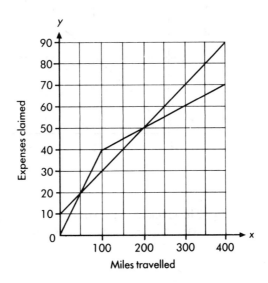

Fig. 8.50

d)   i) Where the graphs intersect is $x = 50$ and $x = 200$.
     ii) $50 < x < 200$.
     iii) £90 − £70 = £20.
     iv) Look at the graph to see where the vertical difference is worth just £10. This
         happens when $x = 0$, $x = 100$, $x = 300$, although I don't think the school inspector
         would claim when $x = 0$. So the two values would be just $x = 100$ and $x = 300$.

A4

Draw the line $2x + 3y = 6$ first, which is a straight line as illustrated in Fig. 8.51.

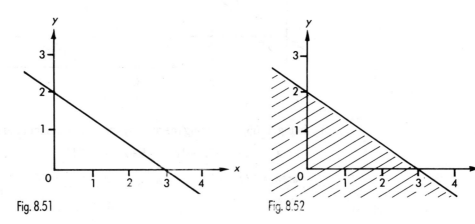

Fig. 8.51   Fig. 8.52

Then consider any point, say, (0,0), substitute it into the inequality and you get $0 + 0 \geqslant 6$. This is not true hence this is the region we do *not* want, and therefore in this question the one that needs shading out (see Fig. 8.52). Do not *touch* the line $2x + 3y = 6$, as this line is included in the region wanted.

A5

a)   Your graph should look like that in Fig. 8.53.

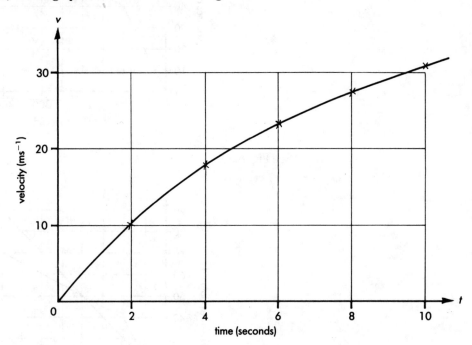

Fig. 8.53

b)   The gradient of the straight line in Fig. 8.54 is $28 \div 8 = 3.5$ and the significance of this is that this represents the actual acceleration of the car after 4 seconds.

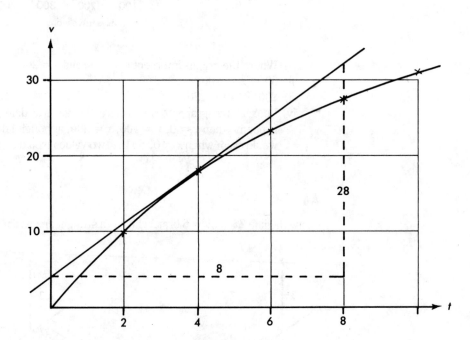

Fig. 8.54

c)   In Fig. 8.55, estimating the area by the trapezium method gives us

$$- \text{area} = \frac{2}{2} \{0 + 2(10+18+23.5+27.5) + 31\}$$

$$\text{area} = 189.$$

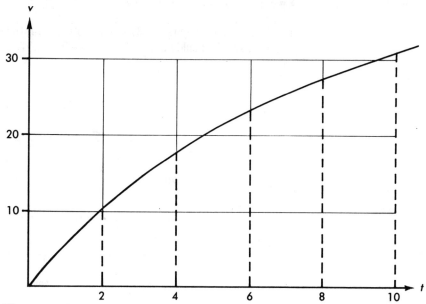

Fig. 8.55

The significance of this is that it represents the total distance covered over the 10 seconds which will be 189 metres.

A6

a)   See Fig. 8.56.

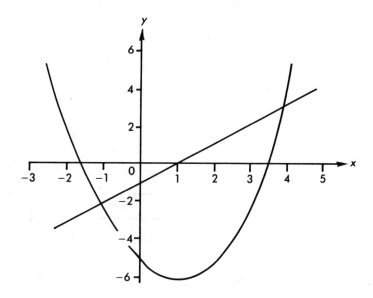

Fig. 8.56

b)   The solution set is found at points where the intersection of these curves is, which is the point where $x = -1$ and $x = 4$.

c) $x^2 - 2x - 5 = x - 1 \rightarrow x^2 - 2x - x - 5 + 1 = 0$
$$\rightarrow x^2 - 3x - 4 = 0.$$

d)   You need to evaluate $(x^2 - 2x - 5) - (x^2 - x - 11) = -x + 6 = 6 - x$.
Now, from the given equation $x^2 - x - 11 = 0$, we see that adding $6 - x$ to both sides gives $(x^2 - x - 11) + (6 - x) \quad = 6 - x$
$$\rightarrow x^2 - 2x - 5 = 6 - x.$$
You now need to draw the line $y = 6 - x$ and find its point of intersection with $y = x^2 - 2x - 5$. Doing this will give you the solutions $x = 3.9$ and $x = -2.8$.

A7

a) The missing heights are 24, 30, 32, 30, 24, 14, 0, respectively.
b) Your graph should look something like Fig. 8.57.

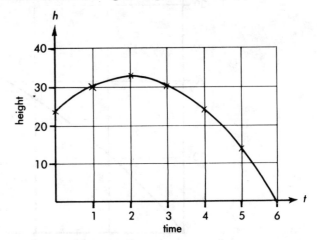

Fig. 8.57

c)   i) Height of the cliff is where the graph starts on the y-axis, 24 metres.
   ii) Up to 32 metres, 8 metres higher than the cliff-top.
   iii) Hits the sea when $h = 0$, this is when $t = 6$, i.e. after 6 seconds.
   iv) You need to draw a tangent to the curve at $t = 5$, which will give you a straight line
       of gradient $= \dfrac{36}{4} = -9$ metres per second, but this is velocity, and the speed is the

   velocity with no sign, so the speed is 9 metres per second.

A8

a) Surface area given by $2 \times (hx + hx + x^2) = 4hx + 2x^2$, and since the total surface area
   is 72 cm^2, then $4hx + 2x^2 = 72 \rightarrow 4\,hx = 72 - 2x^2$

$$h = \frac{72 - 2x^2}{4x} = \frac{18}{x} - \frac{x}{2}$$

b) Volume $=$ length$\times$breadth$\times$height
          $= x \times x \times h$

$$= x^2 \left(\frac{18}{x} - \frac{1}{2}x \right) = 18x - \frac{1}{2}x^3.$$

c)   The table should be completed as in Fig 8.58.

x	0	1	2	3	4	5	6
v	0	17.5	32	40.5	40	27.5	0

Fig. 8.58

d)   The graph will look like Fig. 8.59.

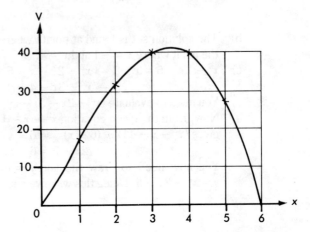

Fig. 8.59

e) Read from the graph above when V = 30 metres. There are two values, $x = 1.8$ and 4.8; but since we are told that $h > x$, then from where

$$h = \frac{18}{x} - \frac{x}{2} \text{ then } \frac{18}{x} - \frac{x}{2} > x \rightarrow \frac{18}{x} > \frac{3x}{2}$$

$$\rightarrow 12 > x^2 \rightarrow x < 3.5$$

So the solution we seek is $x = 1.8$ cm (from the graph), hence $h = 9.1$ cm.

A9

a) See Fig. 8.60.

Fig. 8.60

Time (hours)	0	½	1	1½	2	2½	3	3½	4
Number of bacteria	25	50	100	200	400	800	1600	3200	6400

b) i) The graph will be like that in Fig. 8.61.

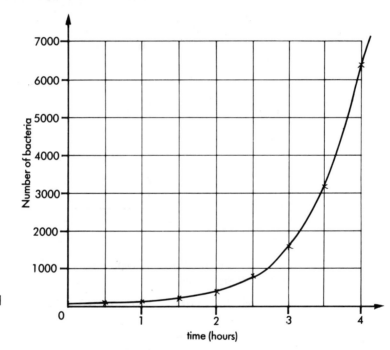

Fig. 8.61

ii) Read from the graph when the bacteria reach 2500 – it is after 3.3 hours (3 hours 18 minutes).

c) After 10 hours the number has doubled 20 times, hence 25×2^{20}, which will be 26 214 400 or 26 million.

A10

a) 10 000 litres per hour for 7 hours = 70 000 litres
15 000 litres per hour for 2 hours = 30 000 litres
giving a total of 100 000 litres.
Looking at the graph, if we calculate the area of the two rectangles as in Fig. 8.62, the area = (10 000 × 7) + (2 × 15 000) = 100 000, the same as above. So the area beneath the graph is the amount of water put into the pool.

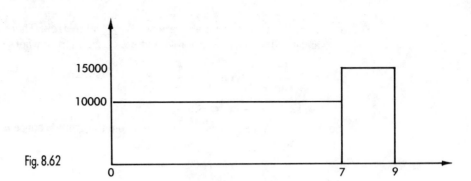

Fig. 8.62

b) i) From midnight the rainfall steadily increases until 1 am. From 1 am to 2.30 am, it is a continuous downpour, then it gradually decreases until at 3 am it had stopped raining.

ii) The shape is a trapezium of area $\dfrac{100}{2}(1\tfrac{1}{2} + 3) = 225$ litres.

iii) Height of water, h metres $\propto$ amount of water put in, w litres, i.e. $h \propto w$. Hence $h = kw$ (k being a constant).
When $w = 100\ 000$, $h = 2 \rightarrow 2 = 100\ 000\ k \rightarrow k = 0.00002$.
So when $w = 225$, representing the extra water put in, the rise in height will be given by
$$h = 0.00002 \times 225 \text{ metres}$$
$$= 0.0045 \text{ metres} = 0.45 \text{ cm}.$$

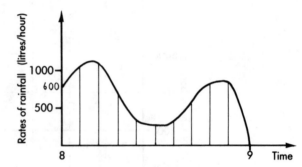

Fig. 8.63

c) Split the shape up into trapeziums as in Fig. 8.63, then using the trapezium rule width of 2½ little squares, which will represent a time of 0.1 hour. The area will be given by:
$$\text{area} = \frac{0.1}{2}[600 + 2(1050 + 1100 + 700 + 300 + 250 + 300 + 600 + 800 + 850) + 0]$$
$$= 625 \text{ litres}.$$

A11

a) Since the differences of V are all the same (0.50), then if the relationship between V and d gave a straight line the differences between d would also be constant. Here they are 0.63, 1.26, 1.66, 1.81, 2.65, gradually increasing and *not* constant. So the graph of (V,d) is *not* going to be a straight line.

b) See Fig. 8.64.

Fig. 8.64

V^2	0.25	1.00	2.25	4.00	6.25	9.00
d	0.52	1.15	2.41	4.07	5.88	8.53

c) i) Because if you draw the graph of V^2 against d you do get points that look as if they lie in a straight line, and so this shows that the relationship is of the form $d = aV^2 + b$, where a will be the gradient of that straight line, and b the d-axis intercept.

ii) Where gradient $= \dfrac{8.75}{8.01} = 1.09$ and d-axis intercept $= -0.32$.

Hence $d = 1.09\,V^2 - 0.32$.

A STUDENT'S ANSWER WITH EXAMINER'S COMMENTS

a) Copy and complete the table for values of y where

$$y = 2x - 7 + \frac{10}{x}$$

x	1	1.5	2	2.5	3	3.5	4
y	5	2·7	2	2	2·3	2·9	3·5

Good, correct answers, rounded off to a suitable degree of accuracy.

b) Draw an x-axis, using a scale of 4 cm to 1 unit. Draw a y-axis using a scale of 2 cm to 1 unit.
Plot the points from your table and draw the graph of

$$y = 2x - 7 + \frac{10}{x}$$

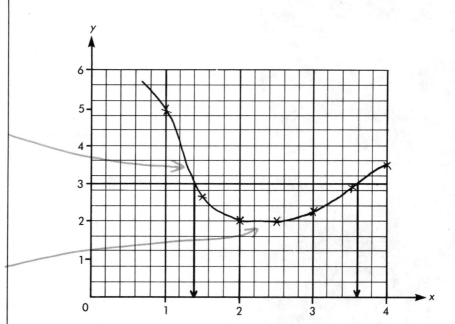

Points plotted correctly, but the curve is rubbish! Here is a bump! It should be a smooth curve.

A poor flat bottom! This should have been rounded to give a smooth curved bottom.

c) Use the graph to find the minimum value of $2x - 7 + \frac{10}{x}$ for values of x between 1 and 4.

answer 2

Answer wrong because of the flat bottom. Unlikely to be given any credit here at all.

d) By drawing a suitable straight line on your graph parallel to the x-axis, find the approximate solutions of

$$2x + \frac{10}{x} = 10.$$

$x = 1·35$ $x = 3·59$

Excellent, well done, drawn in the correct line of $y = 3$ and found the intersection with the curve accurately from your graph.

You are obviously a good student, but have thrown marks away with a sloppy curve. Would still score well with this answer.

GETTING STARTED

At the Higher Level of mathematics, the knowledge of *geometrical facts* is expected. These will often have been explored during coursework in school or college, but they do need *learning* for the examination. In the exam it is how you *apply* your knowledge of geometrical facts that gains you marks. So be familiar with the 'rules of the geometrical game'. These will then give you the confidence to search through a geometrical problem to find the correct solution.

In an *extension paper* you are unlikely to be given a formula sheet, so do learn all the facts outlined in this chapter.

USEFUL DEFINITIONS

Allied	Supplementary angles on one side of a transversal, facing each other.
Complementary	Angles that add up to 90°.
Diagonal	A line joining two corners of a geometrical shape.
Edge	The line where two faces meet.
Equilateral	Having same lengths.
Face	The surface of a solid shape bounded by edges.
Polygon	A plane shape with many straight sides.
Rhombus	A parallelogram with all its sides the same length.
Subtend	Two lines that meet and form an angle.
Supplementary	Angles adding up to 180°.
Tessellation	A plane shape that will fill a complete plane and leave **no** spaces.
Transversal	A straight line that crosses through at least two parallel lines.
Vertex	A point where two lines or edges meet.

ESSENTIAL PRINCIPLES

1 > ANGLES

There are a lot of geometrical facts involving *angles*. You are advised to learn them all. This will then arm you with the weapons necessary for problem solving and for recognising the different situations that these geometrical facts apply to.

POLYGONS (having N sides)

The total of the exterior angles is **always** 360°.
The total of the interior angles is 180 (N − 2)°.

REGULAR POLYGONS (having N sides)

A *regular polygon* is one that has all its sides the same length and where each exterior angle is equal.

Then: the size of each exterior angle is given by $\dfrac{360°}{N}$

the size of each interior angle is given by $180° - \dfrac{360°}{N}$.

ISOSCELES TRIANGLE

An *isosceles triangle* has two sides the same length, and the angles opposite to these equal sides are always equal (see Fig. 9.1). The vertical angle bisector will also be the perpendicular bisector of the opposite side as shown here. This will give us two congruent triangles, as shown in Fig 9.2.

Fig. 9.1

Fig. 9.2

TRAPEZIUM

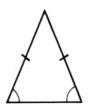

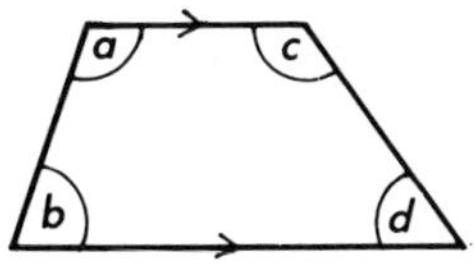

Fig. 9.3

A *trapezium* is a quadrilateral that has two sides parallel as shown in Fig. 9.3. The pairs of angles made with each transversal are allied angles, that is they add up to 180° (e.g. $a + b = 180° = c + d$).

CIRCLES

From any chord in a *circle*, all the angles subtended on the same arc are equal (see Fig. 9.4).

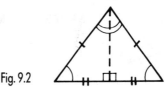

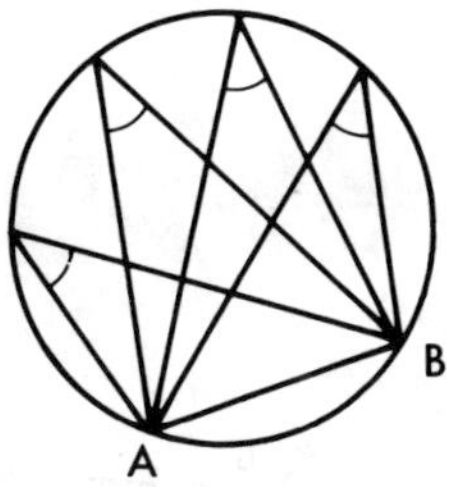

Fig. 9.4

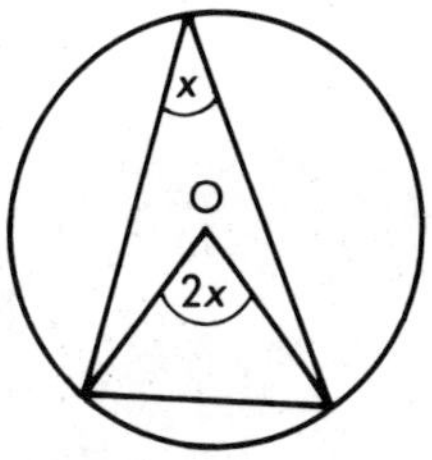

Fig. 9.5

From any chord in a circle, the angle subtended at the centre is double any angle subtended at the arc of the circle in the same segment (see Fig. 9.5).

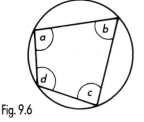

Fig. 9.6

Any quadrilateral drawn so that its four vertices touch the circumference of the same circle is said to be *cyclic*. The opposite angles will add up to 180°, e.g. in Fig. 9.6, $a + c = 180°$, $b + d = 180°$. Any quadrilateral that has its opposite angles adding up to 180 will be cyclic and so a circle can be drawn around the vertices.

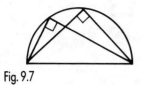

Fig. 9.7

If any triangle is drawn in a semi-circle with one side the diameter and its opposite angle on the arc (as in Fig. 9.7), then this angle made at the arc is a right angle.

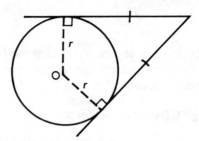

Fig. 9.8

Tangents to a circle will be perpendicular to the radius of the circle. Intersecting tangents form an isosceles triangle (see Fig. 9.8).

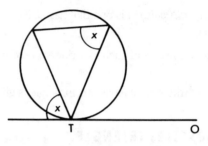

Fig. 9.9

> **Now see how many of these facts you've remembered, go on, test yourself.**

Where OT is a tangent at T, then the angles indicated (x) are equal, this being called the 'alternate segment' theorem (see Fig. 9.9).

2 > INTERSECTING CHORD THEOREM

This can quite easily be shown by drawing and measuring, and will probably have been part of your coursework.

INTERNAL INTERSECTING

In Fig. 9.10, chords AB and CD intersect each other at X, then AX.XB = CX.XD.

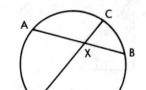

Fig. 9.10

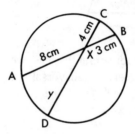

Fig. 9.11

WORKED EXAMPLE 1

In Fig. 9.11, find y.
We can use the intersecting chord theorem to say AX.XB = CX.XD,

hence $8 \times 3 = 4 \times y$

$\rightarrow \quad \dfrac{8 \times 3}{4} = y = 6$ cm.

EXTERNAL INTERSECTING

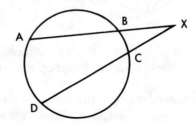

Fig. 9.12

In Fig. 9.12, the **same** rule works also, i.e. AX.XB = CX.DX

WORKED EXAMPLE 2

In Fig. 9.13, find y.

Using the theorem AX.XB = CX.XD, then $(5 + 2) \times 2 = 3 \times (y + 3)$
$$\rightarrow 14 = 3y + 9$$
$$14 - 9 = 3y = 5$$
$$y = \frac{5}{3} \text{ cm.}$$

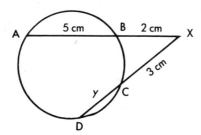

Fig. 9.13

TANGENTS

Where XT is a *tangent* to the circle at T then the intersecting chord theorem is AX.XB = XT².

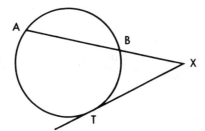

Fig. 9.14

EXERCISE 1

Where TC is the tangent to the circle, find the lengths of   i) p,   ii) q.

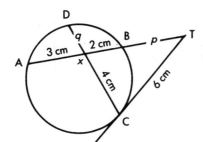

Fig. 9.15

3 CONGRUENCY

Congruent shapes are exactly the same in size and shape (although one shape may well be a reflection of the other).

In mathematic examinations it is usual for this to be tested within triangles where certain minimum pieces of information can tell us that the two triangles are congruent. These pieces of information are:

■ SSS → all three sides equal in length.
  Figure 9.16 shows △ ABC congruent to △ XYZ.

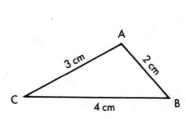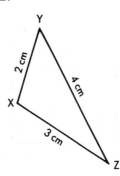

Fig. 9.16

- AAS or ASA → two angles the same (which is the same as all three angles the same!), and a corresponding side equal. Figure 9.17 shows △ ABC congruent to △ PQR.

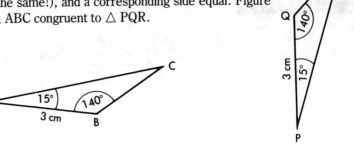

Fig. 9.17

- SAS → Two sides and the included angle equal. Figure 9.18 shows △ ABC congruent to △ FEG.

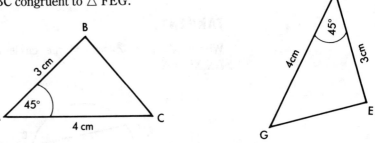

Fig. 9.18

NB. Notice how each letter must correspond exactly to its angle, e.g. if ABC is congruent to XYZ, then A = X, B = Y, C = Z and AB = XY, BC = YZ, CA = ZX.

EXERCISE 2

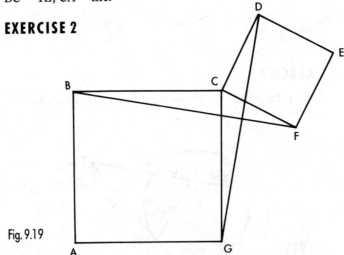

Fig. 9.19

In Fig. 9.19, ABCG and CDEF are both squares. Find a pair of congruent triangles.

4 ▷ SYMMETRY

Marks are easily lost in this section due to careless errors... don't you make them.

You ought to be familiar with the *symmetries* of plane figures, i.e. *line symmetry* and *rotational symmetry*.

LINE SYMMETRY

If you could imagine folding a shape over so that one half fits exactly on top of the other half, then the line over which you have folded is called a *line of symmetry*.

The examples in Fig. 9.20 are of shapes with their lines of symmetry shown as dotted lines.

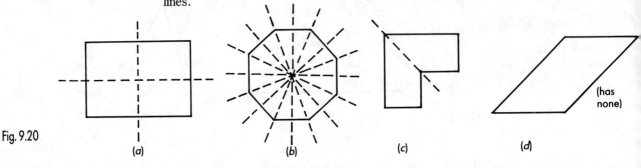

Fig. 9.20

(a)   (b)   (c)   (d)

ROTATIONAL SYMMETRY

This is sometimes called 'point symmetry'. The order of *rotational symmetry* is 'the number of times a shape fits into a tracing of itself in one full rotation'.

The examples in Fig. 9.21 are of shapes with the order of rotational symmetry indicated. Look and check you can see why each shape will have that particular order.

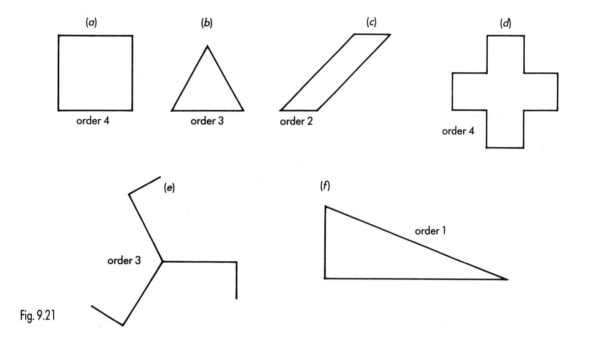

Fig. 9.21

EXERCISE 3

i) Sketch a shape with 3 lines of symmetry
ii) Then sketch a different shape with rotational symmetry of order 3.

3D SYMMETRY

This is 'similar' to plane symmetry in that it has two types;
planes of symmetry and *axes of symmetry*.

Planes of symmetry

A solid shape has a *plane of symmetry* if you can 'slice' the shape into two matching pieces, one the exact mirror image of the other. One way to find these planes of symmetry is to visualise the shape being cut and to see in your imagination whether the pieces are matching mirror images or not.

WORKED EXAMPLE 3

Find how many planes of symmetry the triangular prism in Fig. 9.22 has.

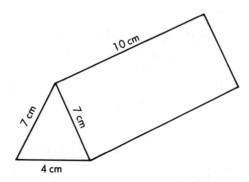

Fig. 9.22

Consider the prism, it can be cut into two exact halves, as shown in Fig. 9.23. Hence the shape has two planes of symmetry.

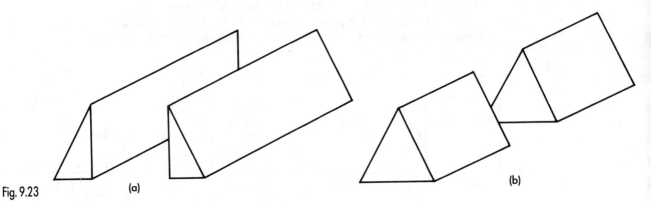

Fig. 9.23   (a)   (b)

Axes of symmetry

An *axis of symmetry* is a line around which the shape may rotate and yet still occupy the same space. For example, in the cuboid shown in Fig. 9.24 there are three axes of symmetry.

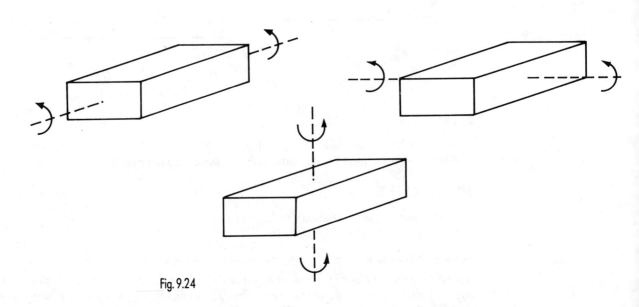

Fig. 9.24

The order of rotational symmetry around any axis of symmetry is the 'number of times a shape could occupy the same space in one full rotation'.

EXERCISE 4

What are the symmetries of a square based pyramid?

5 ▷ GEOMETRICAL DRAWING

Even at the highest level of GCSE mathematics you are quite likely to be asked to draw or construct a particular plane shape. It could be to find out a result or to solve some problem by a scale drawing.

You need to be confident about drawing to scale information about a particular bearing by the use of a protractor, remembering always to start by drawing in your *North* line.

WORKED EXAMPLE 4

From home, Jenny flew a plane 30 km on a bearing of 150°, then flew at a bearing of 060° until landing at Cleethorpes Airport. She flew straight back on a bearing of 260°. How far is her home from Cleethorpes Airport?

If we use a scale drawing of 1 cm to represent 10 km, then we can easily draw Jenny's journey to Cleethorpes in Fig. 9.25, except as yet we do not know where she stopped.

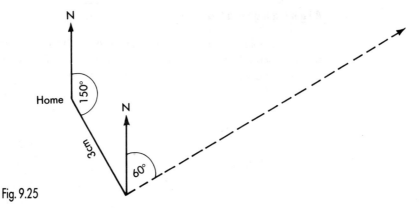

Fig. 9.25

Now, since home is a bearing of 260° from Cleethorpes, then Cleethorpes must be on a bearing of 260 − 180 = 80° from home. Draw this line in to give us the situation in Fig. 9.26. We can now see where Cleethorpes Airport is and measure the distance. It will be 8.9 × 10 km = 89 km.

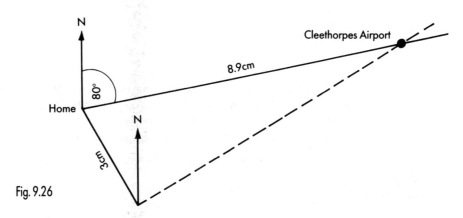

Fig. 9.26

CONSTRUCTIONS

You need to confidently perform the following constructions:

Line bisector

By making two arcs from either end of the line and draw a straight line through the points of intersection. Figure 9.27 illustrates this method of bisecting the line CD. It is worth noting that this line is properly called the 'perpendicular bisector'.

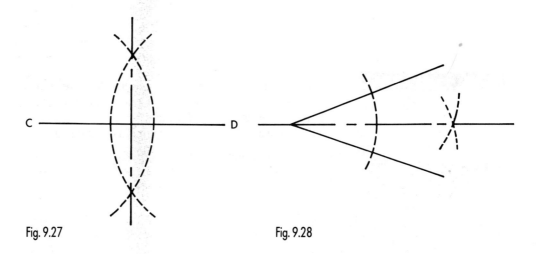

Fig. 9.27   Fig. 9.28

Angle bisector

From the vertex of the angle, draw an arc through both sides of the angle. Then from these points of intersection, arc into the middle of the space between the angles. Where these two arcs cross over join to the vertex of the angle for the angle bisector. This is illustrated in Fig. 9.28.

Right angle at a point

From the point P where the right angle needs to be drawn, arc on both sides. (You may need to extend the line to be able to do this.) From these two arcs just construct a line bisector. This will be a perpendicular line at the point where you want it. This is illustrated in Fig. 9.29.

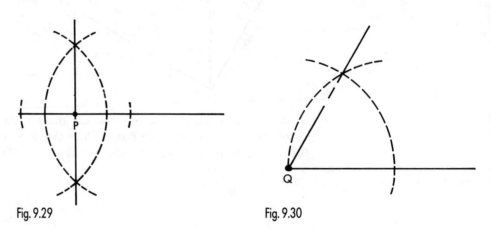

Fig. 9.29   Fig. 9.30

60° angle

From the point Q where you want the 60°, arc a quarter turn to just intersect with the line where you want the angle. Then from that intersection, with the same size arc, arc a quarter turn to go from your original point to intercept with the previous quarter turn. Join this point of intersection with the original point to give 60°. This is shown in Fig. 9.30.

Perpendicular from a point, R, to a line

From the given point, R, draw an arc big enough to cut the line twice. Then from these cuts, construct on the other side of the line, a perpendicular bisector between them; join this up to the given point R and you have your perpendicular. This is illustrated in Fig. 9.31.

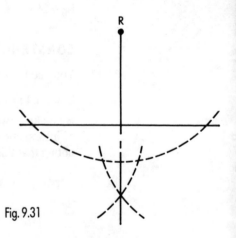

Fig. 9.31

6 **LOCI**

Loci are the paths of moving points that usually have some pattern to them. You are quite likely to be asked to find the locus of a point, but there are some locus situations that you ought to be familiar to start off with.

The *locus* of a point moving so that it is a constant distance from:

1 a point A; is a circle (see Fig. 9.32).

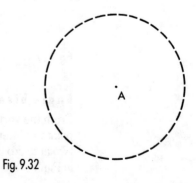

Fig. 9.32

2 two fixed points, A and B; is the perpendicular bisector of the line joining those two points (see Fig. 9.33).

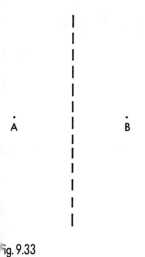

Fig. 9.33

3 a line AB; is a 'racetrack' shape, made up of two parallel lines and two semi-circles (see Fig. 9.34).

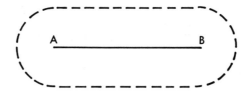

Fig. 9.34

4 two lines AB and DC; is the angle bisector of the angle that both lines subtend to (see Fig. 9.35).

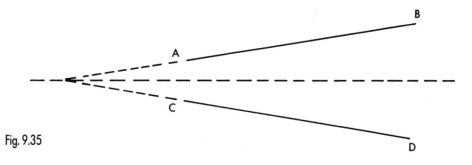

Fig. 9.35

WORKED EXAMPLE 5

Draw the locus of the point P which is always 1 cm away from the rectangle ABCD in Fig. 9.36.

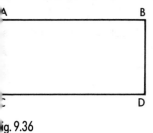

Fig. 9.36

You can see from Fig. 9.37 that the distances easily worked out are those vertically perpendicular 1 cm from the straight edges.

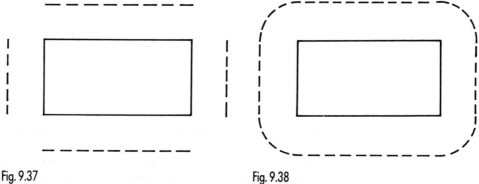

Fig. 9.37   Fig. 9.38

We then need to consider the point, P, 1 cm away from each vertex A, B, C and D. These will be quarter circles joining the given straight lengths already to give the final locus as in Fig. 9.38.

EXERCISE 5

Construct an equilateral triangle of side 4 cm, then draw the locus of the point, P, which is 1 cm away from the triangle (and not inside it).

SOLUTIONS TO EXERCISES

S1

i) To find p, use AT.TB = TC^2 $\quad\rightarrow (5 + p) \times p = 36$
$\rightarrow 5p + p^2 = 36$ $\qquad\qquad \rightarrow p^2 + 5p - 36 = 0$
which solves to give $p = 4$ and $p = -9$, the negative answer here has no use to us, so
we take the solution $p = 4$.

ii) To find q, use AX.XB = XC.XD $\quad\rightarrow 3 \times 2 = 4 \times q$

$$\rightarrow 6 = 4q \rightarrow q = \frac{3}{2}$$

S2

By identifying which line is equal to which, and which angles are the same, you should have
found that BCF and GCD are congruent.

S3

There are many different possible answers here, and I offer two possible answers to each,
but there are a lot more.

i) See Fig. 9.39, **or** Fig. 9.40.

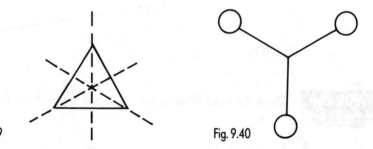

Fig. 9.39   Fig. 9.40

ii) Both the above shapes do have rotational symmetry of order 3. Yet two more examples
are shown in Fig. 9.41.

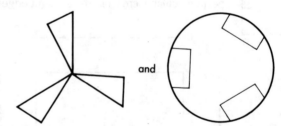

and

Fig. 9.41

S4

The square-based pyramid shown in Fig. 9.42 has four planes of symmetry all through the
vertex and where M, N, P and Q are midpoints of AD, DC, BC, AB respectively. The
planes can be described as going through the points MVP, QVN, AVC and DVB. The
shape will also have an axis of symmetry vertically down through the vertex V.

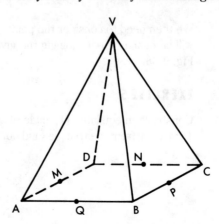

Fig. 9.42

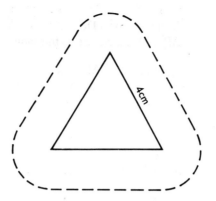

Fig. 9.43

S5

You will have a shape looking something like Fig. 9.43. With three straight sides of length 4 cm, each parallel to one side of the equilateral triangle, then the curved parts are each arcs of circles with radius 1 cm having the centres the vertices of the triangle.

EXAMINATION TYPE QUESTIONS

HIGHER LEVEL

Q1

In Fig. 9.44 angle EAD = 40° and angle AFB = 60°. Calculate the size of angle AED, giving reasons for each step of your calculation. (NEA; 1988)

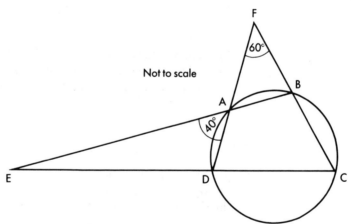

Fig. 9.44

Q2

In this question you must give valid reasons for your answers. Numbers on their own will not be sufficient. Figure 9.45 shows the cross section of a tunnel. The tunnel is circular

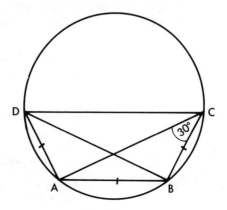

Fig. 9.45

with a platform DC in it. The platform is held by five rods AB, AD, BC, BD and AC. Rods AB, AD and BC are all the same length. The angle between AC and BC is 30°.

a) Find i)∠ADB; ii)∠ABD; iii)∠DBC; iv)∠BDC.
b) i) Explain how you know that platform DC must be parallel to rod AB.
    ii) What does the answer to a) iii) tell you about DC?   (WJEC; 1988)

Q3

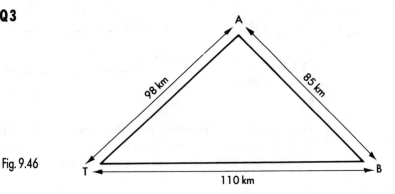

Fig. 9.46

Figure 9.46 shows the location of a television transmitter (T) in relation to two towns Amburg (A) and Beetown (B).

a) Using a scale of 1 cm to represent 10 km, draw an accurate scale diagram of the triangle TAB.

> *Use your pair of compasses for the curve to be accurate.*

b) The transmitter has a range of 80 km. Draw accurately, on your scale drawing, the curve which represents the limiting range of the transmitter.

It is planned to build a repeater station, R, which is an equal distance from both Amburg and Beetown.

c) On your drawing, construct accurately the line on which the repeater station must be built.

The repeater station is to be built at the maximum range of the transmitter.

d) i) Mark with the letter R the position of the repeater station on your diagram.
    ii) Find the minimum transmitting range of the repeater station so that programme can be received in Amburg. Give your answer in km, to the nearest km.
                                                                        (LEAG; 1988)

Q4

Figure 9.47 shows the outline of a 50p piece. O is the centre.
a) i) Work out the sizes of the angles marked x and y.
    ii) Correct your answers to the nearest ½ degree.

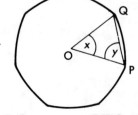

b) Work out $x + 2y$ using your answers to a) ii).
c) Explain why the answer to b) is not 180°.

Fig. 9.47   (MEG; 1988)

Q5

Figure 9.48, which is drawn to scale, shows a wheel, centre A, of radius 25 cm which rolls along the ground and then mounts a step of height 15 cm. Draw the resulting locus of A as the wheel approaches the step, mounts it and then moves on.
                                                                        (NEA; 1988)

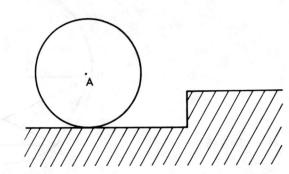

Fig. 9.48

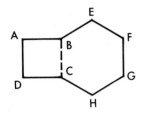

Fig. 9.49

Q6

a) The tile ABEFGHCD in Fig. 9.49 is made up of a square ABCD attached to a regular hexagon BEFGHC along their common side BC. What is the size of i)∠ABC; ii)∠EBC; iii)∠ABE?

b) Tiles of the same shape as ABEFGHCD are placed in the pattern shown in Fig. 9.50.

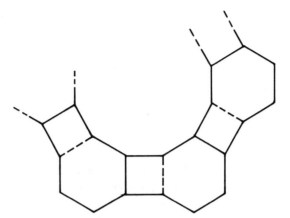

Fig. 9.50

    i) Without drawing the completed figure, explain why the tiles will form a closed shape if the pattern is continued.

    ii) The completed shape encloses a regular polygon. How many sides has this polygon? (WJEC; 1988)

Q7

Figure 9.51 shows a cyclic quadrilateral ABCD with AB parallel to DC. The line TAS is the tangent to the circle at A. Angle DAT = 47° and angle BAS = 52°.

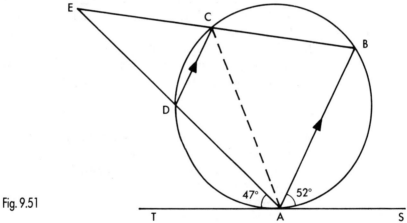

Fig. 9.51

a) Find the size of i) angle ACB; ii) angle DCA; iii) angle CBA.

The lines BC and AD are produced to meet at E.

b) Show that the triangle EBA is isosceles.

The triangles ECD and EBA are similar such that EC:CB = 2:3.

c) Calculate the value of $\dfrac{\text{area of triangle ECD}}{\text{area of triangle EBA}}$ (LEAG; 1988)

Q8

Figure 9.52 shows part of a tessellation.

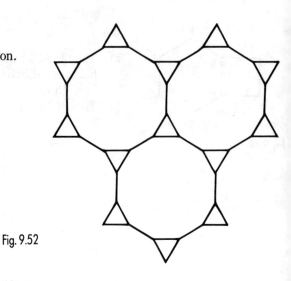

Fig. 9.52

a)   Mark a line of symmetry and label it *m*.
b)   Mark a point labelled P about which the tessellation has rotational symmetry of order 3.

(MEG; 1988)

EXTENSION   **Q9**

a)   The country of Futuria is one vast horizontal plain. As part of its national defences, a straight electronic strip, 20 km long and of negligible width, is built along the ground. This emits delta-rays, which cause radio jamming anywhere within 10 km of any point of the strip. Draw, on a scale of 1 cm to 4 km, the region on the ground that is affected by the jamming.

b)   The influence of the strip also extends into the atmosphere, so that there is a region above the ground affected by the radio jamming. Describe the shape of this region in words, using the names of mathematical figures.

c)   Foreign aircraft are required to fly across Futuria horizontally at a height of 8 km above the ground. The Ministry of Aviation issues charts showing the region affected by the jamming at this height. Draw, on the same scale as a), the shape of this region.

d)   In another part of the country there is a strip with similar properties in the shape of a letter L, each arm of the L being 10 km long. Draw, on the same scale as a), the region on the ground affected by jamming from this strip.   (O and C; 1988)

Q10

a)   Figure 9.53 shows the proposed vertices of a planar network (that is, a network in which no edges cross over one another). Also, each vertex is to be joined to each other vertex by one edge (but not more than one). Draw this network, and answer the following questions about it:

   i) What are the values of V, R and E, the numbers of vertices, regions and edges? (Do not forget to count the outside region.)

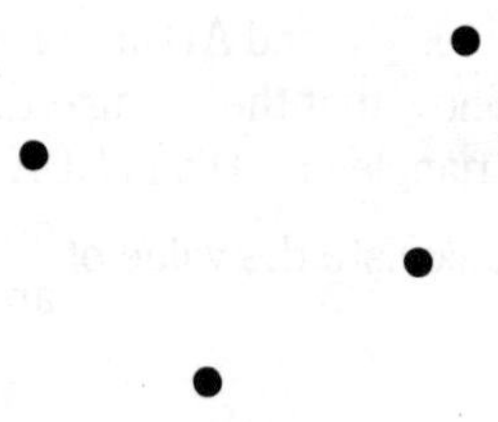

Fig. 9.53

   ii) What is the degree of each vertex?
   iii) Check that $V + R - E = 2$. (This is called Euler's rule.)
   iv) How many edges are there on the boundary of each region?

b) The problem in this part of the question is to draw a different planar network: each vertex is to be joined to exactly three other vertices, and there are to be four edges on the boundary of each region.

    i) Give a reason why E must be equal to $\frac{3}{2}$V.

    ii) Give a reason why E must be equal to 2R.

    iii) Use Euler's rule to calculate the values of V, R and E.

    iv) Make a drawing of this network.

c) Now consider the problem of drawing a planar network in which each vertex is joined to exactly four other vertices, and in which there are five edges on the boundary of each region.

    i) Write down equations connecting E with V, and E with R.

    ii) Use Euler's rule to calculate the values of V, R and E.

    iii) What do you deduce about this network?

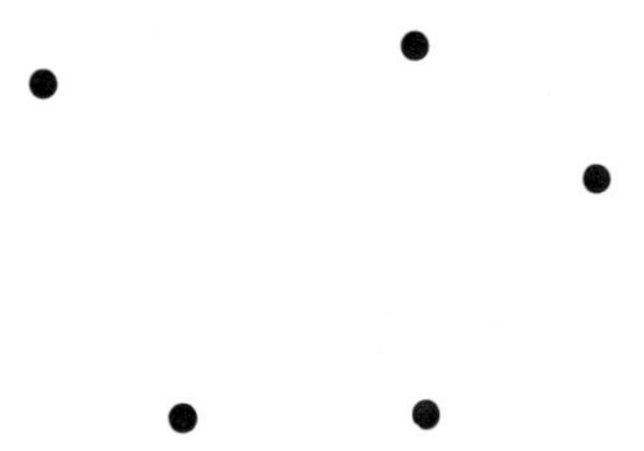

Fig. 9.54

d) Figure 9.54 shows how a doodler marked five points on a sheet of paper, and tried to join each vertex to each other vertex by one edge, in such a way that no edges crossed over one another. Prove that, however he tried to do it, he would not be successful.

(O and C; 1988)

Q11

a) Mark two points A and B on your paper, 8 cm apart. By choosing various pairs of numbers (not necessarily both whole numbers) which multiply together to give 20, plot a number of points P on your paper with the property that PA $\times$ PB = 20, (where both PA and PB are measured in centimetres). Hence draw as accurately as you can, the locus of points with this property.

b) Starting again with a new pair of points A and B, still 8 cm apart, draw the locus of points with the property PA $\times$ PB = 16.

c) Repeat b) with the property PA $\times$ PB = 15.

d) The three loci which you have drawn should all look different, but they all have the same kinds of symmetry. Name, with reference to the points A and B,

    i) any lines of reflective symmetry,

    ii) the centre and order of any rotational symmetry, for all three loci.

    Describe a simple shape which has the same symmetry as these loci.

e) All the loci in a), b) and c) have a property of the form PA $\times$ PB = K, where K is a number. For some values of K, there are points where the locus cuts the line between A and B. Suppose that it does this at a point P where PA = x cm.

    i) What is the length PB in terms of x?

    ii) Show that x satisfies the quadratic equation $x^2 - 8x + K = 0$.

    iii) For the values K = 16 and K = 15, solve this equation for x.

    iv) Show that, if K = 20, the equation has no solution for x.

    v) Use these results to explain why the loci have different forms for these three values of K.

(O and C; 1987)

OUTLINE ANSWERS TO EXAM QUESTIONS

A1

You should work it out on the diagram first, then state the route that gets you to the answer in the shortest (but correct) way.

BAF = 40° . . . opposite angles equal.
BAD = 140° . . . angles on a line add up to 180°.
BCD = 40° . . . cyclic quadrilateral, opposite angles add up to 180°.
FDC = 80° . . . angles in a triangle add up to 180°.
ADF = 100° . . . angles on a line add up to 180°.
AED = 40° . . . angles in a triangle add up to 180°.
Hence AED = 40°.

A2

a)   i) ADB = 30° it is from the same chord AB that angle ACB is from, hence ADB = ACB.
    ii) ABD = 30° since triangle ABD is isosceles and so ABD = ADB.
    iii) Since DAB = 120°, angles in a triangle add up to 180°, then DCB = 60°, because opposite angles in a cyclic quadrilateral add up to 180°.
        Also BAC = 30°, since ABC is an isosceles triangle where BAC = BCA.
        Hence CDB = 30°, it is from the same chord BC that angle BAC is from. Finally DBC = 90° since DBC, BCD and CDB add up to the angles of a triangle and hence 180°.
    iv) BDC = 30°, having found it on the way to DBC.
b)   i) Because the angles DCB and CBA add up to 180° and in their position are allied angles, meaning that BC is the transversal so DC and AB are parallel.
    ii) That DC is the diameter of the circle.

A3

Your final diagram should look like Fig. 9.55.

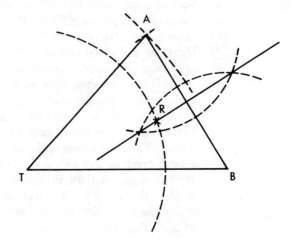

Fig. 9.55

d)   ii) The minimum range is the distance from A to the point R which is 45 km.

A4

a)   i) $x = 360 \div 7 = 51.43°$ $y = \frac{1}{2}(180 - 51.43) = 64.29°$
    ii) $x = 51.5°$ $y = 64°$
b) $x + 2y = 51 + 2 \times 64 = 179.$
c)   Due to both x and y having been rounded down.

A 5

The locus will follow the dotted line shown in Fig. 9.56.

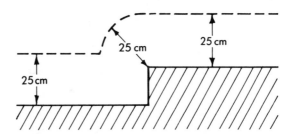

Fig. 9.56

You do need to find the centre when the wheel has just touched the step for the first time, since that is where the locus changes from the straight line to the curve, of centre top vertex of step.

A 6

a)   i) 90°   ii) $180 - \left(\dfrac{360}{6}\right) = 120°$

   iii) $360° - (90 + 120) = 150°$.

b)   i) Because they fit together forming a regular shape where the inside edges are a regular polygon of exterior angles shown in Fig. 9.57, and thirty is a factor of 360, hence they will all fit together with $\dfrac{360}{30} = 12$ so 12 edges are needed, hence 6 tiles are being used.

   ii) The polygon has $\dfrac{360}{30} = 12$ sides.

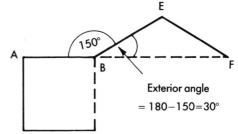

Fig. 9.57

Exterior angle
= 180−150=30°

A 7

a)   i) 52° (alternate segment theorem).
   ii) 47° (alternate segment theorem).
   iii) $180 - (52 + 47) = 81°$ (CBA and BCD being allied angles).

b)   Angle DAB $= 180 - (52 + 47) = 81°$ (angles on a line add up to 180). Hence angle DAB = angle CBA, and triangle EBA is isosceles.

c)   If EC:CB = 2:3 then EC:(EC + CB) = 2:5. So the ratio of the lengths of △ ECD and △ EBA is 2:5, and the ratio of the area of the triangles is $2^2:5^2 = 4:25$,

   hence $\dfrac{\text{area of } \triangle \text{ ECD}}{\text{area of } \triangle \text{ EBA}} = \dfrac{4}{25}$

A 8

a)   There are three possible lines you could have chosen. You should have just *one* of the dotted lines shown in Fig. 9.58 as the line of symmetry.

Fig. 9.58

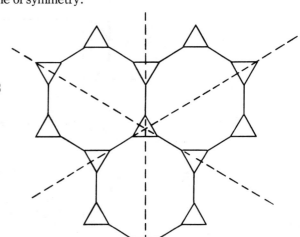

b)   The point P should be on Fig. 9.58 in the position where the three dotted lines all meet, which shows that the centre of *any* of the triangles could be a possible P.

A9

a) See Fig. 9.59.

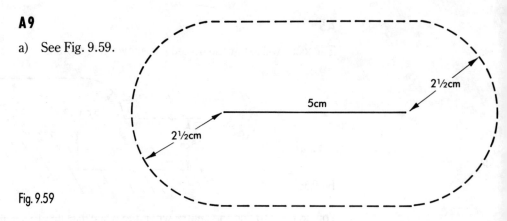

Fig. 9.59

b) At each end the shape will be one half of a hemisphere of radius 10 km, then between them will be half a cylinder with regular cross section being a semi circle of radius 10 km.

c) Consider the semi circle cross section of the middle, shown in Fig. 9.60. The dotted line represents the limit of the unsafe area.

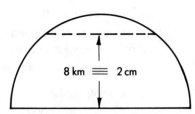

Fig. 9.60

Consider the front elevation of the atmospheric 'shape' shown in Fig. 9.61. Again the dotted line indicates the limit of the unsafe area.

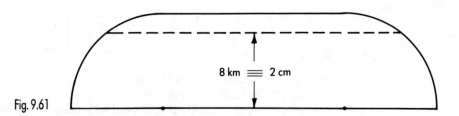

Fig. 9.61

So on the plan of the shape, by using the end and front elevation, you can fix the bounds of this region, as shown in Fig. 9.62.

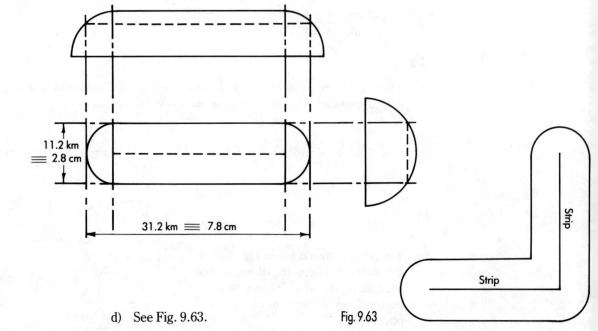

Fig. 9.62

d) See Fig. 9.63.

Fig. 9.63

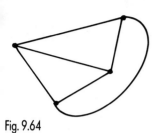

Fig. 9.64

A10

a)   See Fig. 9.64.
   i) $V = 4, R = 4, E = 6.$ ii) 3
   iii) $4 + 4 - 6 = 2.$ Yes.   iv) 3

b)   i) Each vertex has 3 edges coming from it, so you would have $E = 3V$, but each edge is joined to 2 edges, hence you halve the total number of edges, so $E = \dfrac{3V}{2}$ (see Fig. 9.65).

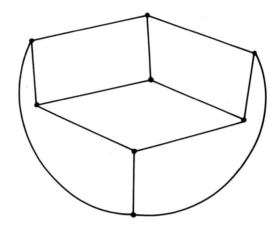

Fig. 9.65

   ii) Since 4 edges bound each region, then this would give $E = 4R$, but each edge is used to form two regions, hence $E = \dfrac{4R}{2}$ which gives $E = 2R$.

   iii) Using $V + R - E = 2$ and $E = \dfrac{3}{2}V \rightarrow V = \dfrac{2E}{3}$
       and $E = 2R \rightarrow R = \frac{1}{2}E.$
       Substitute for V and R gives
       $\dfrac{2E}{3} + \dfrac{1}{2}E - E = 2 \rightarrow \dfrac{7E}{6} - E = 2 \rightarrow \dfrac{E}{6} = 2 \rightarrow E = 12.$

       If $E = 12$, then $V = 8$ and $R = 6$.
   iv) This is the drawing given to start with, which is possibly the best way to start the problem!

c)   i) By following the pattern found in the last part, here you would get
       $E = \dfrac{4V}{2} \rightarrow E = 2V$

       and $E = \dfrac{5}{2} R$
   ii) From Euler's rule $V + R - E = 2.$
       Substitute $V = \dfrac{E}{2}$ and $R = \dfrac{2E}{5} \rightarrow \dfrac{E}{2} + \dfrac{2E}{5} - E = 2 \rightarrow E = -20.$

       If $E = -20$, then $V = -10$ and $R = -8$.
   iii) That it is impossible to draw.

d)   Trying to do that is to try and make i) each vertex joined to exactly 4 other vertices and so each region would be bounded by 3 edges.
   This will imply the relationship $E = \dfrac{4V}{2}$ and $E = \dfrac{3R}{2}.$
   So solving $V + R - E = 2$ when $E = 2V$ and $E = \dfrac{3R}{2}$
   $$\rightarrow V = \dfrac{1}{2}E \text{ and } R = \dfrac{2}{3}E.$$
   Substituting gives us $\dfrac{1}{2}E + \dfrac{2}{3}E - E = 2 \rightarrow \dfrac{7}{6}E - E = 2$
   $$\rightarrow E = 12.$$
   $E = 12 \rightarrow R = 8$ and $V = 6$.
   So you need 6 vertices to do this and so it is impossible with only 5.

A11

a) Using pairs of numbers like (2,10), (10,2), (4,5), (5,4), (2½,8), (8,2½), etc. you should end up with a locus like Fig. 9.66.

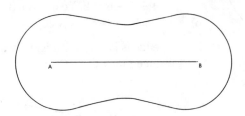

Fig. 9.66

b) See Fig. 9.67.

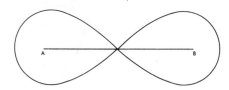

Fig. 9.67

c) See Fig. 9.68.

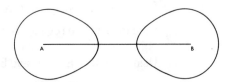

Fig. 9.68

d) i) All have 2 lines of symmetry, one along the line AB, the other along the perpendicular bisector of AB.
   ii) Rotational symmetry of order 2 about the midpoint of line AB.
   (All rectangles (that are not squares) have the same properties.)

e) i) $8 - x$.
   ii) Since PA × PB = K, where PA = x and PB = $8 - x$
      then $x(8 - x) = K \rightarrow 8x - x^2 = K \rightarrow 0 = K - 8x + x^2$
      $\rightarrow x^2 - 8x + K = 0$.
   iii) When K = 16
      $x^2 - 8x + 16 = 0 \rightarrow (x - 4)(x - 4) = 0$
      $\rightarrow x = 4.$
   When K = 15
      $x^2 - 8x + 15 = 0 \rightarrow (x - 3)(x - 5) = 0$
      $\rightarrow x = 3$ and $x = 5$
   iv) When K = 20
      $x^2 - 8x + 20 = 0.$
   If we tried to solve by using the formula $x = \dfrac{-b \pm \sqrt{b^2 - 4ac}}{2a}$

   where $a = 1, b = -8, c = 20,$

   then $x = \dfrac{-b \pm \sqrt{(64 - 80)}}{2}$

   But note $\sqrt{-16}$ is impossible, hence there is no solution.
   v) The solutions to $x^2 - 8x + K = 0$ are the possible distances AP where P is the point that the loci crosses AB.
      Each different value of K here gives a different type of quadratic equation.
      When K = 16, the equation has only one solution, hence the loci only crosses AB once.
      When K = 15, the equation has two solutions, hence the loci cross AB twice.
      When K = 20, the equation has no solutions, hence the loci does not cross AB at all.

A STUDENT'S ANSWER
WITH EXAMINER'S COMMENTS

Question

The diagram, which is drawn to a scale of 1 cm to represent 1 m, shows a rod OA of length 3 m which is pivoted at a point O on a horizontal table so that it can rotate in a vertical plane. A light is positioned at L, 5 m vertically above O, as a result of which the rod casts a shadow OP on the table.

When the size of angle LOA is $x°$, the length of the shadow OP is y metres.

By drawing different positions of OA and measuring, construct a table of possible values of y against x for $0 \leqslant x \leqslant 90$. Draw a graph to show how y varies as x increases from 0 to 90 and hence determine the greatest possible value of y.

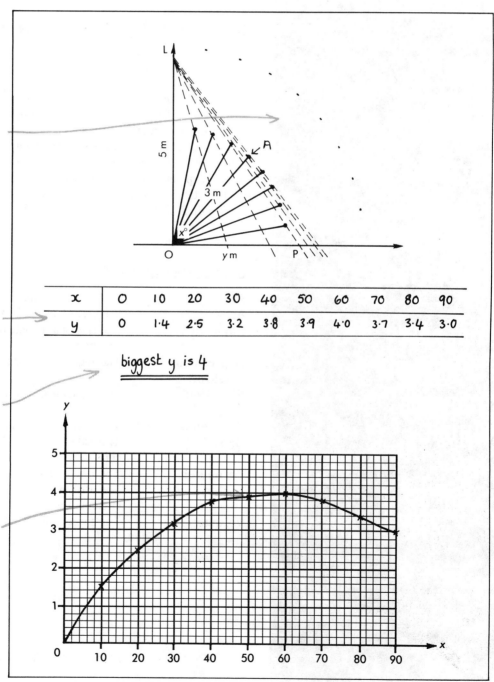

❝ Good to see the systematic approach of measuring every 10°, although it is not clear particularly around $x = 40°$ ... 90°. **❞**

x	O	10	20	30	40	50	60	70	80	90
y	O	1·4	2·5	3·2	3·8	3·9	4·0	3·7	3·4	3·0

biggest y is 4

❝ The table confirms the correct approach to the problem, but the accuracy could be better as the graph indicates. **❞**

❝ From this graph the answer is correct and would gain credit. **❞**

❝ The points have been plotted correctly and the axes are just what was asked for — well done. The funny dip at x = 50° should have indicated an error and this particular piece of data should have been checked. **❞**

❝ Poor drawing resulted in wrong information being used and lost marks. (The correct answer should be 3.75 cm, try and show this to yourself.) **❞**

MENSURATION

GETTING STARTED

This topic is all about calculating lengths, areas and volumes of given shapes and solids, or even distances from one place to another. It is a vital link between arithmetic and algebra. In the vast majority of cases you will need a *formula* to substitute into. These formulae are best learned, then you will have the confidence that you are armed with the right equipment for problem solving. At the Higher Level of GCSE mathematics a lot of the problems to solve are 3D situations in which you have to think abstractly about the situation.

There will be many questions set in your mathematics examination that relate to this chapter.

USEFUL DEFINITIONS

Arc	Part of the circumference of a circle.
Area	Flat space included in a boundary.
Adjacent	The side of a triangle next to the angle concerned and the right angle.
Depression (angle of)	The angle measured below the horizon.
Elevation (angle of)	The angle measured above the horizon.
Hypotenuse	The longest side of a right angled triangle.
Opposite	The side of a triangle opposite the angle concerned.
Perimeter	The length round all the outside of a flat shape.
Sector	The area of a circle bounded by two radii and the circumference.
Volume	The space inside a 3 dimensional shape.

ESSENTIAL PRINCIPLES

1 ▷ PERIMETER

It is essential that you understand the meaning of perimeter is the total outside length of a flat shape. The one you must learn is the perimeter of a circle, which is given by:

circumference = $\pi \times$ diameter of circle   or   C = πD.

2 ▷ AREA

You must *learn* the following facts:

■ **Rectangle**

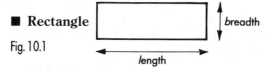

Fig. 10.1

area is length $\times$ breadth.

■ **Parallelogram**

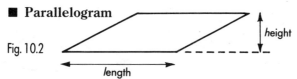

Fig. 10.2

area is length $\times$ height.

■ **Triangle**

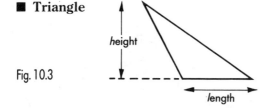

Fig. 10.3

area is $\frac{1}{2} \times$ base length $\times$ height.

■ **Trapezium**

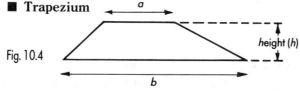

Fig. 10.4

area is $\frac{1}{2} \times$ height $\times$ sum of parallel lengths $= \dfrac{h}{2}(a + b)$.

■ **Circle**

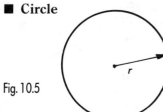

Fig. 10.5

area is πr^2.

■ **Sector**

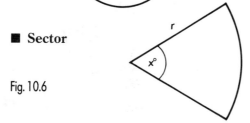

Fig. 10.6

area is $\dfrac{x}{360} \cdot \pi r^2$

> ❝Do try to learn them, it saves a lot of time and helps you to see the solution more clearly.❞

Although some of these will be on a formula sheet, it will give you much more confidence if you know them and are familiar with them all.

3 ▷ VOLUME

You should be familiar with the following two formulae for finding *volumes*. In an examination a formula might well be given, but it will help you in confidence and to see what is the appropriate method to use if you actually know these formulae yourself.

Prisms

Many of our regular mathematical shapes are *prisms*, and the volume of any prism is found by:

Volume = length $\times$ (regular cross sectional area)

In a prism the regular cross section is the same as the area of the end, hence the formula is perhaps better remembered as volume = length × end area.

Pyramids

The volume of any pyramid or cone is given by:

Volume = (height × base area) ÷ 3.

WORKED EXAMPLE 1

The cone shape in Fig. 10.7 is full of water. The water is poured into the cup shown next to it. What will be the depth of water in the cup?

Volume of water in the cone = $\frac{1}{3} \times 8 \times$ end area = $\frac{1}{3} \times 8 \times \pi \times 3^2 = 24\pi$ (I keep it in terms of π as I do not want to have to do any rounding off until the very end of the question). The volume of water inside the cup is given by

(end area) × height = $\pi \times 2.5^2 \times h$

but as the volume we are interested in is 24π then we can set up the equation

$$\pi \times 2.5^2 \times h = 24\pi$$
$$\rightarrow h = \frac{24\pi}{\pi \times 2.5^2} = 3.84$$

Hence the depth of water will be 3.8 cm.

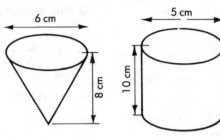

Fig. 10.7

Sphere

The volume of a sphere of radius r is given by

Volume = $\frac{4}{3}\pi r^3$

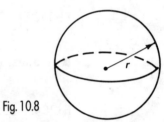

Fig. 10.8

EXERCISE 1

Into a cone cornet of diameter 5 cm and a height of 12 cm, was placed a sphere of ice cream of diameter 5 cm. It melted, yet all stayed inside the cone. What depth of the cone was filled with the melted ice cream. (Assume the melted ice cream will have the same volume as the frozen ice cream.)

Fig. 10.9

4 ▷ SURFACE AREA

There is no regular pattern here to follow, so use your mathematical wits and common sense, being sure to remember the surface areas of the tops and bottoms. Outlined below are some particular solids and how to find their total surface area.

■ **Cylinder**

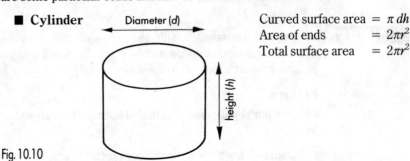

Curved surface area = $\pi\,dh$
Area of ends   = $2\pi r^2$ (2 ends)
Total surface area = $2\pi r^2 + \pi dh$.

Fig. 10.10

■ **Sphere**

Fig. 10.11

Surface area $= 4\pi r^2$

■ **Cone**

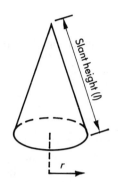

Fig. 10.12

Curved surface area $= \pi rl$
Area of end $= \pi r^2$
Total surface area $= \pi r^2 + \pi rl$

EXERCISE 2

The earth has a diameter of 12762 km. Two thirds of the earth is covered by water. What will be the total surface area of all the water in the seas and lakes in the world?

5 ▷ PYTHAGORAS

You should be familiar with the theory of Pythagoras, which is illustrated in Fig. 10.13.

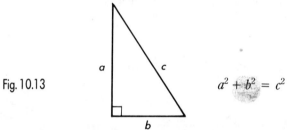

Fig. 10.13 $\qquad a^2 + b^2 = c^2$

WORKED EXAMPLE 2

The regular octagon in Fig. 10.14, of side 13 cm, was being cut out of a square piece of card. What is the smallest sized piece of card that this could be?

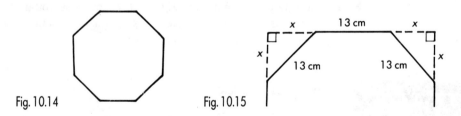

Fig. 10.14 Fig. 10.15

Consider one end of the card, the corners cut off form a right angled triangle with the hypotenuse 13 cm and the smaller sides the same length of x, as in Fig. 10.15.

Hence $x^2 + x^2 = 13^2$ $2x^2 = 169$ $x^2 = 84.5$ $x = 9.2$ cm.

So the length of the square will be $13 + (2 \times 9.2) = 31.4$ cm.

EXERCISE 3

Draw a right angled triangle and then construct a semi-circle on each side in Fig. 10.16.

i) See if the area of the two smaller semi-circles add up to the area of the large one.
ii) Do you think this will always be the case?

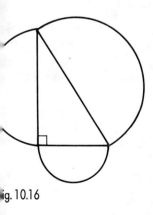

Fig. 10.16

6 ▶ TRIGONOMETRY

You must be familar with the simple trig' ratios found in right angled triangles, illustrated in Fig. 10.17.

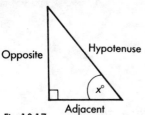

Fig. 10.17

$$\tan x = \frac{\text{opposite}}{\text{adjacent}} \qquad \sin x = \frac{\text{opposite}}{\text{hypotenuse}} \qquad \cos x = \frac{\text{adjacent}}{\text{hypotenuse}}$$

Note, we use the abbreviated form of the trigonometrical ratios of:

> tan . . . for tangent
> sin . . . for sine
> cos . . . for cosine
> and trig . . . for trigonometry

No one gets a grade A without being able to do trigonometry, so do try to take it all in and learn as much off by heart as you can.

You must be able to recognise when trig is needed and be able to quickly recognise which of the trig ratios to use, tan, sin or cos. You will need to use trig if you wish to find:

> angles from information about lengths
> or lengths from information about angles and length.

You need to be familiar with the above trig ratios to enable you to go straight to the correct trig ratio. Try the following way of spotting which is needed from the involved sides:

No hypotenuse . . . use tan

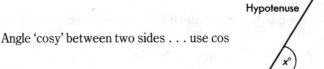

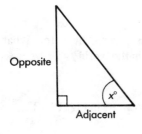

Fig. 10.18

Angle 'cosy' between two sides . . . use cos

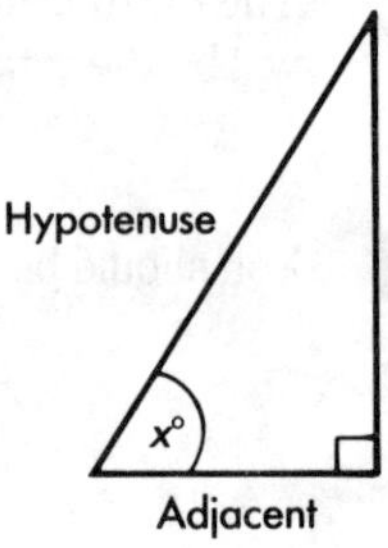

Fig. 10.19

Side next to angles (adjacent) not involved . . . use sin

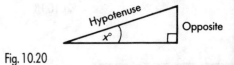

Fig. 10.20

Use any way of being able to recognise which to use, but do find one that *you* can remember. (Try "Tommy On A Ship Of His Caught All Herring".)

The way you set out your trig questions can lose you marks, so do be careful, set out correctly, use correct trig statements, and unless told otherwise 'round off to one more significant figure than the given information'.

WORKED EXAMPLE 3

In Fig. 10.21, calculate x.

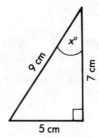

Fig. 10.21

$$\text{Cos } x = \frac{7}{9} = 0.777. \text{ (Use INV cos or cos}^{-1} \text{ on your calculator.)}$$

$$x = 39°.$$

WORKED EXAMPLE 4

In Fig. 10.22, find x.

$$\frac{x}{5} = \tan 70 \rightarrow x = 5 \tan 70$$
$$x = 13.7 \text{ cm.}$$

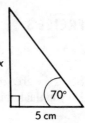

Fig. 10.22

WORKED EXAMPLE 5

In Fig. 10.23, find x.

$$\frac{4}{x} = \sin 65 \rightarrow \frac{4}{\sin 65} = x$$

$$x = 4.41 \text{ cm.}$$

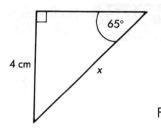

Fig. 10.23

Note the kind of information that you need to write down as your solution, it's not much but it's vital to be correct. At this high level, you will lose marks for not writing down your trig statements as above . . . be warned!

EXERCISE 4

A regular pentagon is drawn inside a circle of radius 8 cm. Find the length of one straight edge of the pentagon.

SPECIAL TRIG FACTS

You may have discovered the following facts in your coursework; if not then try yourself to show that they are true:

$$\tan x = \frac{\sin x}{\cos x} \text{ and } (\sin x)^2 + (\cos x)^2 = 1.$$

At this stage, these facts do not have a lot of use, but they do 'come into their own' at A level – look out for them.

7 ▷ TRIGONO-METRICAL GRAPHS

You need to be able to recognise the special features about the graph of each trig function, so that you can sketch them when necessary.

THE SINE CURVE

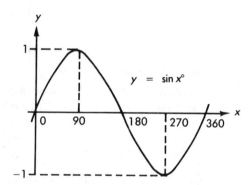

Fig. 10.24

In Fig. 10.24, see how the sine of angles between 0 and 180 are positive, and the sine of angles between 180 and 360 are negative.

WORKED EXAMPLE 6

Solve the equation $\sin x = 0.5$ $(0 < x < 180)$.
Using $\sin^{-1}x$ on the calculator gives $x = 30°$, but look at the graph and you will see that there are two angles with a sine of 0.5. One is 30° (check with the calculator). Now, from the symmetry of the graph you can see that the other angle will be $(180 - 30)$ which is 150°.

Hence $x = 30°$ and $x = 150°$.

Check then from the graph that:

for $0 < x \leqslant 180$ $\sin(180 - x) = \sin x.$
for $180 < x \leqslant 360$ $\sin(180 + x) = -\sin x.$

Play about with these two facts on your calculator and show to yourself that they are true. They are difficult facts to learn, but if you learn the shape of the sine curve and its main points then you can always work them out again for yourself.

Sketch the graph of $y = \sin 3x$ $0 < x < 180$
A table of values can be built as in Fig. 10.25.

x	0	30	60	90	120	150	180
$3x$	0	90	180	270	360	450	540
$y = \sin 3x$	0	1	0	−1	0	1	0

Fig. 10.25

Sketched smoothly this gives Fig. 10.26.

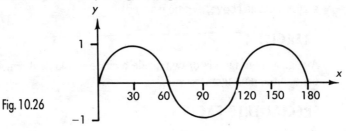

Fig. 10.26

EXERCISE 5

Sketch the graph of $y = 3 \sin x$.

Similar facts and statements can be made about cos and tan. Follow through them now.

THE COSINE CURVE

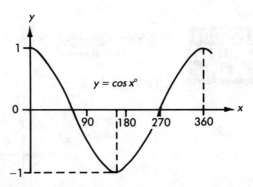

Fig. 10.27

In Fig. 10.27, see how the cosine of angles between 0 and 90, or 270 and 360 are positive, and of angles between 90 and 270 are negative.
From the symmetry of the graph: $\cos (180 - x) = - \cos x$
$$\cos (180 + x) = - \cos x$$
$$\cos (360 - x) = \cos x$$

NB. The sine curve and the cosine curve are exactly the same shape, where the graph of $\cos x$ is just the same as $\sin x$ moved down 90°.

THE TANGENT CURVES

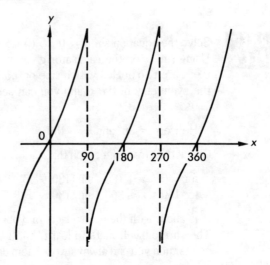

Fig. 10.28

Notice that Fig. 10.28 is a series of parallel curves with what we call 'assymptotes' at $x = 90$ and 270. (But more of that at A level.) It is quite different from the sin and cos curves, yet it still has symmetry to enable us to see that

$$\tan(180 - x) = -\tan x$$
$$\tan(180 + x) = \tan x.$$

EXERCISE 6

Sketch the graphs of $y = \cos 2x$ and $y = \tan x$ to estimate a solution to $\cos 2x = \tan x$. $0 < x < 180$.

ANGLES BIGGER THAN 90°

To find the trig ratio of angles bigger than 90° just press the correct buttons on your calculator, but when given a ratio and you are asked for possible angles, then most calculators will not tell you. You need either to remember the above rules or sketch the graph to remind you.

WORKED EXAMPLE 8

Solve the equation $\cos x = 0.8$. $(0 < x < 360)$

On the calculator $\cos^{-1} 0.8 = 36.9°$.

Also, $\cos(360 - x) = \cos x$, hence where $x = 36.9°$; another solution is $(360 - 36.9)$, which is $323.1°$. So $x = 36.9°$ and $323.1°$.

(You can always easily check the solutions by the use of cos on the calculator.)

EXERCISE 7

Solve the equation $\tan x = 2$ $(0 < x < 360)$

8 ⟩ THE SINE RULE

You may also have come across the sine rule as a piece of coursework; it is a very simple, but useful, fact.

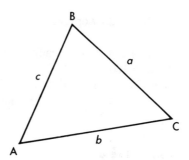

Fig. 10.29

For *any* triangle (label as in Fig. 10.29), then:

$$\frac{a}{\sin A} = \frac{b}{\sin B} = \frac{c}{\sin C} = 2R$$

(where R is the radius of the circumscribed circle, that is the circle that will touch each vertex of the triangle ABC).

Sometimes it is more useful to look at the rule the other way round, that is:

$$\frac{\sin A}{a} = \frac{\sin B}{b} = \frac{\sin C}{c} = \frac{1}{2R}$$

You use the *sine rule* when
    i) you have *not* got a right angle
    ii) you have actual information about one side and its opposite angle
    iii) you have actual information about either one more side or angle.

WORKED EXAMPLE 9

In Fig. 10.30, find x.
Use the sine rule and start with what it is you are looking for.

So $\dfrac{x}{\sin C} = \dfrac{a}{\sin A} \rightarrow \dfrac{x}{\sin 41} = \dfrac{8}{\sin 63}$

$\rightarrow x = \dfrac{8 \times \sin 41}{\sin 63} = 5.9$ cm.

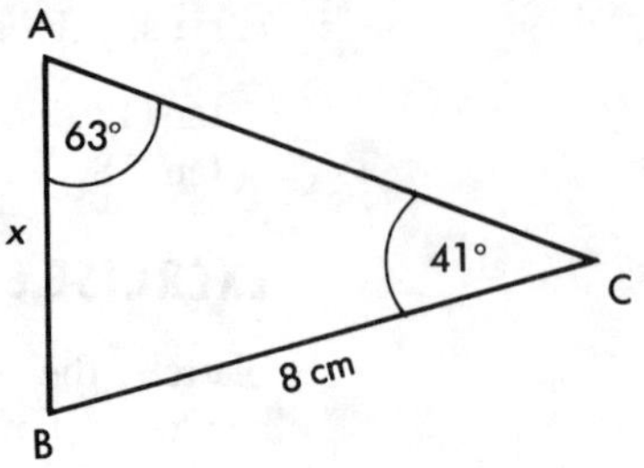

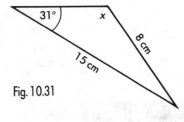

Fig. 10.30

WORKED EXAMPLE 10

In Fig. 10.31, find angle x.

Apply the sine rule to give $\dfrac{\sin x}{15} = \dfrac{\sin 31}{8}$

$\rightarrow \sin x = \dfrac{15 \sin 31}{8} = 0.9657$

giving $x = 74.9°$ or $(180 - 74.9)$
$\qquad x = 74.9°$ or $105.1°$

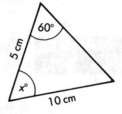

Fig. 10.31

Note: there are sometimes two possible solutions from the sine rule.

WORKED EXAMPLE 11

In Fig. 10.32 find $x°$.

We cannot go straight to x here but to the other unknown angle, let's call it y, then apply

the sine rule: $\dfrac{\sin y}{5} = \dfrac{\sin 60}{10}$

$\rightarrow \sin y = \dfrac{5 \sin 60}{10} = 0.4330$

$\rightarrow \quad y = 25.7$ or $(180 - 25.7) = 154.3$

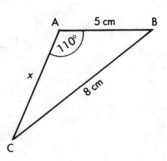

Fig. 10.32

Since one angle is already given as 60°, then another angle cannot be 154.3, since 60 + 154.3 > 180.
Hence $y = 25.7$ and so $x = 180 - (60 + 25.7)$
$\qquad\qquad x = 94.3°$.

EXERCISE 8

In Fig. 10.33, find the length of the side marked x.

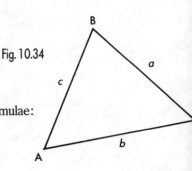

Fig. 10.33

Fig. 10.34

AREA OF TRIANGLES BY SINE RULE

The *area* of any triangle can be found by one of the formulae:
$\qquad$ Area $= \frac{1}{2}ab \sin C$
or Area $= \frac{1}{2}bc \sin A$
or Area $= \frac{1}{2}ac \sin B$.
You can use the sine rule for area of triangle when you know two sides and the angle in between them (the *included* angle).

WORKED EXAMPLE 12	In Fig. 10.35, find the area of triangle ABC. Use the sine rule as: Area $= \frac{1}{2} \times 4 \times 5 \times \sin 120 = 8.7$ cm^2.

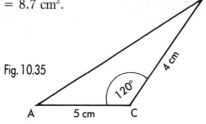

Fig. 10.35

EXERCISE 9

Find the area of the triangle ABC in Fig. 10.36.

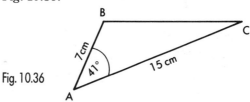

Fig. 10.36

9 > THE COSINE RULE	This rule appears in two different forms and we use each one depending on whether we are calculating a side or an angle.

 Don't use this on a right angled triangle, its too heavy!

1 TO FIND A SIDE

If, as in the 'sine area rule', we are given two sides and the included angle, then we can use the cosine rule as:

$$a = \sqrt{b^2 + c^2 - 2bc \cos A}$$

$$\text{or } b = \sqrt{a^2 + c^2 - 2ac \cos B}$$

$$\text{or } c = \sqrt{a^2 + b^2 - 2ab \cos C}$$

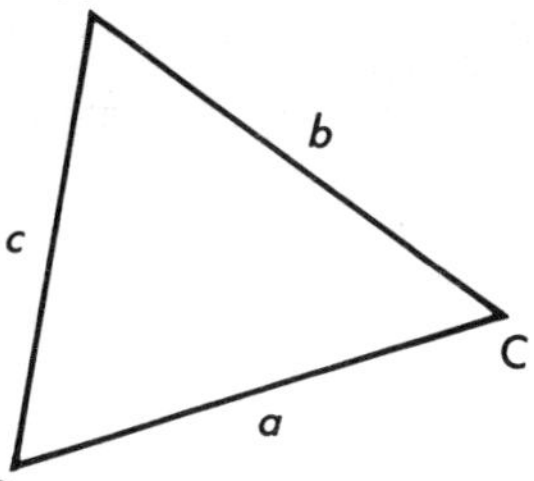

Fig. 10.37

(Look at the pattern of what is given and how you use it.)

WORKED EXAMPLE 13	In Fig. 10.38, find x. Use the cosine rule as:

$$x = \sqrt{(6^2 + 7^2 - 2 \times 6 \times 7 \times \cos 65)}$$

$$= \sqrt{(49.5)}$$

$$x = 7.0 \text{ cm}.$$

Fig. 10.38

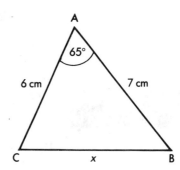

WORKED EXAMPLE 14	In Fig. 10.39, find x. Use the cosine rule as

$$x = \sqrt{(3^2 + 5^2 - 2 \times 3 \times 5 \times \cos 115)}$$

$$= \sqrt{(46.678548)}$$

$$x = 6.8 \text{ cm}$$

Fig. 10.39

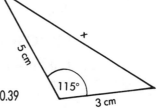

(Note the cos 115 was negative, but should have caused no problems.)

EXERCISE 10

In Fig. 10.40, find x.

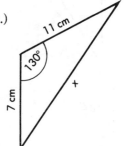

Fig. 10.40

2   TO FIND AN ANGLE

When you know **all** the three sides of a triangle you can use this form of the cosine rule to find any angle:

$$\cos A = \frac{b^2 + c^2 - a^2}{2bc}$$

$$\text{or } \cos B = \frac{a^2 + c^2 - b^2}{2ac}$$

$$\text{or } \cos C = \frac{a^2 + b^2 - c^2}{2ab}$$

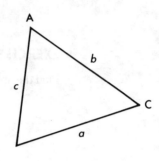

Fig. 10.41

(Look at the pattern of each one and learn the pattern).

WORKED EXAMPLE 15

In Fig. 10.42, find the size of angle A.

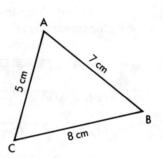

Fig. 10.42

Use the Cosine Rule to give $\cos A = \dfrac{5^2 + 7^2 - 8^2}{2 \times 5 \times 7} = 0.1429$

giving A = 81.8° = 82°

WORKED EXAMPLE 16

In Fig. 10.43, find the size of angle B.

Use the Cosine Rule to give $\cos B = \dfrac{9^2 + 8^2 - 15^2}{2 \times 9 \times 8} = -0.5556$

giving B = 123.7° = 124°.

(Note that if the cosine works out to be negative, the angle will be obtuse.)

EXERCISE 11

In the triangle ABC in Fig. 10.44 calculate the size of the   i) smallest angle   ii) largest angle.

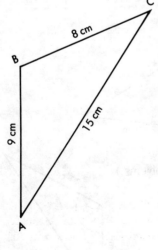

Fig. 10.43

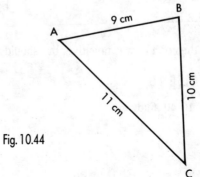

Fig. 10.44

<table>
<tr><td>10 ></td><td>**LATITUDE AND**
LONGITUDE</td></tr>
</table>

This topic only occurs on a very few syllabuses, so do make sure that you need (or want) to look at and revise this part of the chapter. However, you may well find it of interest even if it is not absolutely necessary.

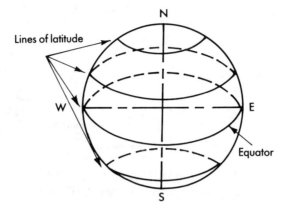

Fig. 10.45

Lines of Latitude (Fig. 10.45) run parallel to the EW direction, and are 'circles' on the earth. The further North from the equator, or South from the equator, the smaller will be the circle. The equator is the largest circle of latitude, having the radius of the earth.

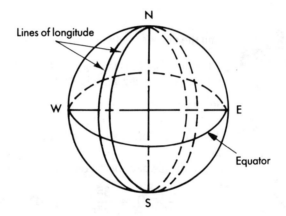

Fig. 10.46

Lines of Longitude (Fig. 10.46) run parallel to the NS direction, and are circles on the earth, all passing through the North and South poles. All circles of longitude have the radius of the earth and as such are called *Great Circles*.

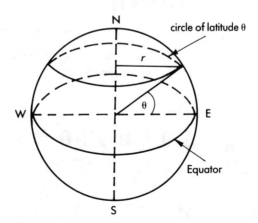

Fig. 10.47

The line of *LATITUDE* θ (Fig. 10.47) always makes an angle of θ when *any* point on that circle of latitude, together with the point on the equator that has the same longitude, subtend an angle of θ at the centre of the earth. It is labelled either north or south depending on which hemisphere it is in.

Note that the radius, r, of the circle of latitude θ is given by $r = R \cos \theta$ where R is the radius of the earth (6381 km).

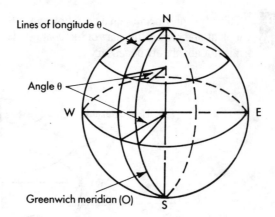

Fig. 10.48

The *Greenwich Meridian* (Fig. 10.48) is the line of longitude 0 and used as a reference point to define all the other meridians (lines of longitude).

For the line of *LONGITUDE* θ, on any circle of latitude there are two points given by:

    i) the Greenwich meridian,   ii) the line of longitude θ.

These two points subtend to an angle of θ perpendicularly to the NS line, as shown in Fig. 10.48.

WORKED EXAMPLE 17

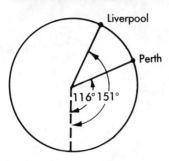

Fig. 10.49

Find the distance between the two towns:

    Perth in Australia having latitude 32° S and longitude 116° East.
    Liverpool having latitude 32° S and longitude 151° East.

Both points are on the same line of latitude, 32°S which has a radius of R cos θ, which here is 6381×cos 32, giving 5411 km. A sketch of the plan of this circle of latitude (Fig. 10.49) illustrates the arc made between Perth and Liverpool has an angle of (151 – 116) which is 35°.

Hence the distance between Perth and Liverpool is given by the arc length where:

$$\text{arc} = \frac{x}{360} \times \pi D = \frac{35}{360} \times \pi \times 2 \times 5411, \text{ which is 3306 km.}$$

You are only going to be asked, even at the extension level, to be concerned with distances round circles of latitude or circles of longitude.

EXERCISE 12

Find the distance between the two cities:

    Leningrad having latitude 60°N, longitude 31°E,
    and Odessa having latitude 46°N, longitude 31°E.

SOLUTIONS TO EXERCISES

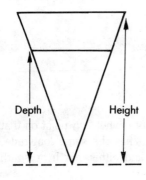

Fig. 10.50

S1

The volume of ice cream is given by $\frac{4}{3}\pi r^3 = \frac{4}{3}\pi \times (2.5)^3 = 65.4 \text{ cm}^3$.
The volume of the cone is given by $\frac{1}{3}\pi r^2 h = \frac{1}{3}\pi \times (2.5)^2 \times 12 = 78.5$.
So the ratio of volume between the melted ice cream and the cone is given by 65.4:78.5 which is 0.8331:1.
The two volumes are similar shapes (see Fig. 10.50) with volume ratio of 0.8331:1, hence a length ratio of $\sqrt[3]{0.8331:1}$ which is 0.941:1.
So the depth of ice cream will be 12×0.941 = 11.3 cm.

S2

Surface area of earth given by $4\pi r^2 = 4\times\pi\times(6381)^2$.
So two thirds will be given by $\frac{2}{3}\times4\times\pi\times(6381)^2 = 3.4\times10^8$ km^2.

S3

i) Yes, they should do: ii) Yes, it will always be the case.

S4

If the pentagon is divided into triangles, then the angle of each triangle at the centre, O, of the circle will be $360\div5 = 72°$ (see Fig. 10.51). The right angled triangle as shown in the diagram can be formed where $x = 72\div2 = 36°$ and its base length, y, is half the side, d, of the pentagon.
Hence $y \quad = 8\sin 36°$
and so $\quad d = 2\times8\times\sin 36 = 9.4$ cm.

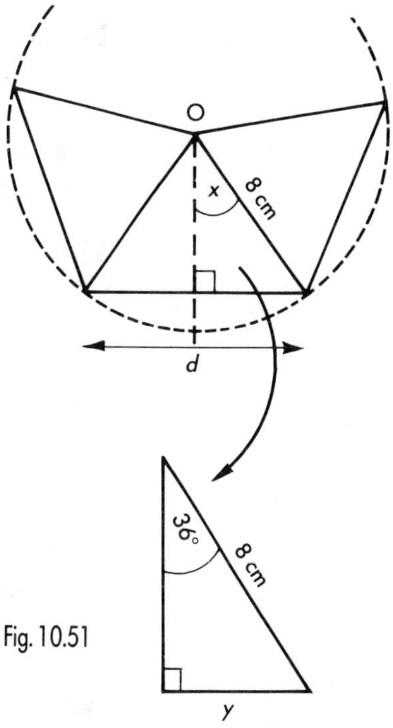

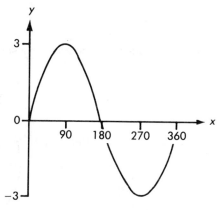

Fig. 10.51

S5

See Fig. 10.52.

Fig. 10.52

S6

See Fig. 10.53. The intersection will be the solution of approximately $x = 28°$.

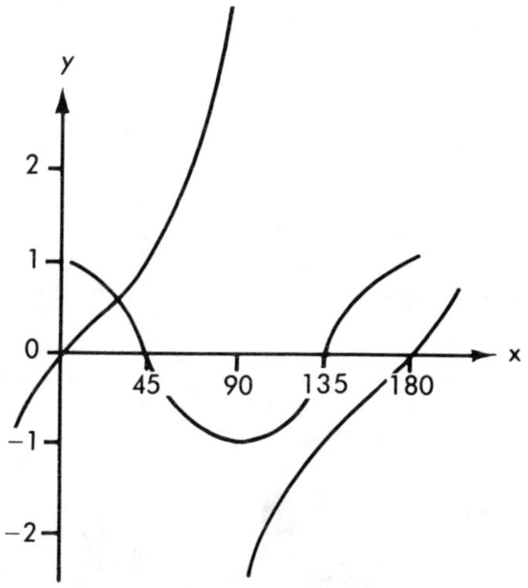

Fig. 10.53

S7

Tan $x = 2 \quad x = 63.4$ and $180+63.4 = 243.4$.

(In any question like this you can always test your answers by finding their tangents on the calculator and checking that indeed they are equal to what you started with.)

S8

Since the information given (see Fig. 10.54) is an angle and its opposite side, no right angle or another side, then first find angle C. I use the sine rule as:

$$\frac{\sin C}{5} = \frac{\sin 110}{8} \rightarrow \sin C = \frac{5\sin 110}{8} = 0.5873$$

$$\rightarrow C = 36°.$$

Then angle B $= 180-(110+36) = 34°$.

Use sine rule again to give $\dfrac{x}{\sin B} = \dfrac{8}{\sin 110}$

$$\rightarrow x = \frac{8\sin 34}{\sin 110} = 4.8 \text{ cm}$$

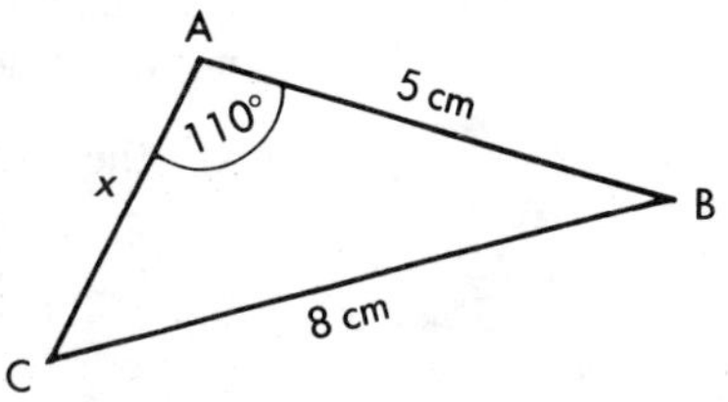

Fig. 10.54

S9

Area $= \frac{1}{2}\times7\times15\times\sin 41 = 34.4$ cm^2.

S10

Use cosine rule to give $x = \sqrt{(11^2+7^2-2\times11\times7\times\cos 130)}$
$= \sqrt{(121+49+99)} = \sqrt{269}$
$x = 16.4$ cm.

(The most common mistake is to forget to square root, but if you are in the correct habit of checking that your answers are sensible then you will spot that error.)

S11

The smallest angle is always opposite the smallest length and similarly, the largest angle is opposite the largest length. Hence smallest angle is opposite the smallest side of 9, hence C. This is found by the cosine rule as:

$$\cos C = \frac{a^2+b^2-c^2}{2ab} \rightarrow \cos C = \frac{10^2+11^2-9^2}{2\times10\times11} = 0.6364$$

$$\rightarrow C = 50.5°.$$

The largest angle is opposite 11, the largest side, hence B. This also is found by the cosine rule to give B $= 70.5°$.

S12

Both points are on the same longitude, hence a circle of radius of the earth (6381 km). The distance between Leningrad and Odessa is the arc of the sector with angle x in Fig. 10.55 $(60-46) = 14°$.

Hence where arc $= \dfrac{x}{360}\pi D$

distance $= \dfrac{14}{360}\times\pi\times2\times6381 = 1559$ km.

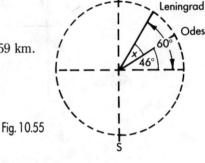

Fig. 10.55

EXAMINATION TYPE QUESTIONS

Q1

Find the value of x such that $90 < x < 180$ and $\sin x° = 0.4567$.   (NEA; 1988)

Q2

Fig. 10.56 shows a metal plate with four quadrants of a circle out away at the corners. Calculate:

a) the radius of the circle of which the quadrants are a part,
b) the total area cut away.   (NISEC Specimen)

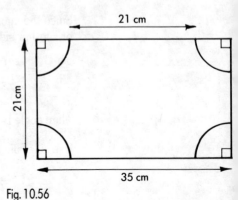

Fig. 10.56

Q3

Figure 10.57 shows that airport A is 400 km from airport B on a bearing of 120°. An aircraft leaves A at 2155 hours to fly to B. Its speed over the ground is 320 km/h.

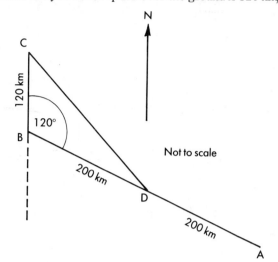

Fig. 10.57

a) Calculate the time at which the aircraft is expected to arrive at B.
b) When the aircraft is at D, halfway between A and B, it is diverted to airport C because of fog at airport B. Airport C is 120 km due North of B.

    i) Calculate the distance from D to C.
    ii) Calculate the bearing of C from D.
    iii) The point on the aircraft's path nearest to B is X. Calculate the distance of X from B.
          (MEG; 1988)

Q4

(In this question, give all distances to the nearest 0.01 km and all angles to the nearest one-tenth of a degree.)

Figure 10.58 represents three villages A, B and C on a hillside. A, C and N are the same height above sea level and N is vertically below B. Angle CAB is 90° and angle BAN is 2.5°. The villages are linked by three straight roads AB, AC and CB, where AB = 8 km and AC = 12 km.

Calculate a) the height of B above N,
              b) the horizontal distance AN,
              c) the horizontal distance CN,
              d) the angle of elevation of B from C.   (LEAG; 1988)

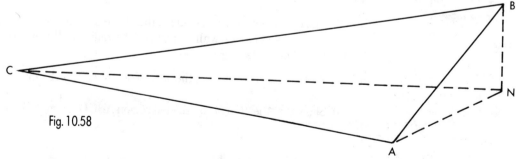

Fig. 10.58

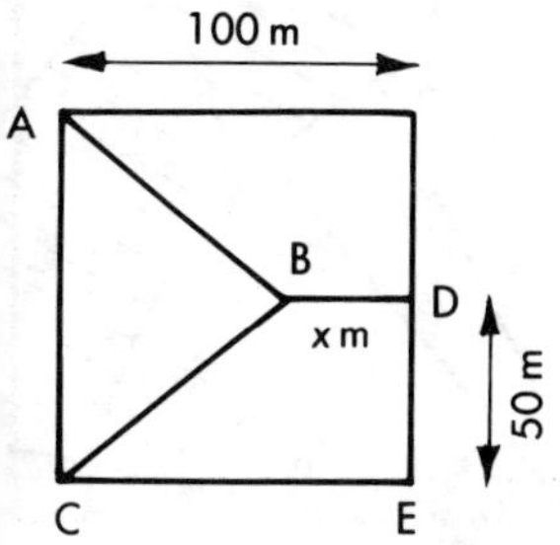

Q5

A field 100 metres square is divided into two trapeziums and a triangle, as shown in Fig. 10.59. BD is x metres long.

a) What is the perpendicular distance from B to AC in terms of x?
b) What is the area of triangle ABC in terms of x?
c) What is the area of trapezium CBDE in terms of x?
d) Each of the three parts of the field has the same area. What is the length of BD?
          (WJEC; 1988)

Fig. 10.59

Q6

The goldfish bowl in Fig. 10.60 is part of a sphere of radius 15 cm. With terms used on the Earth's surface, the base is at Latitude 75°S, the rim at 30°N and the water level is at the equator.

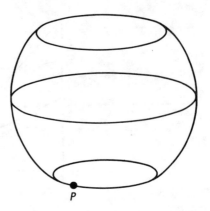

Fig. 10.60

P

a) An insect at P, on the outside of the bowl walks by the shortest route to the rim. How far does it walk?
b) The insect's route is the zero meridian. At the rim it turns right and walks one third of the way round the rim. What are its latitude and longitude now?
c) The insect now walks directly down the inside to the surface of the water. It then swims straight across the water's surface along a diameter. What are the latitude and longitude when it reaches the other side?   MEG; 1988)

Q7

Fig. 10.61

To estimate the volume of timber in the trunk of the conifer in Fig. 10.61, a pupil considered the trunk to be a cone and measured the circumference of the base to be 68 cm. To find the height she walked back 30 m from the base of the tree and took a sighting of the top of the tree. From her eye level (1.2 m above the ground) the angle of the elevation of the top of the tree was 26°.

a) Calculate the height of the tree.
b) Calculate the volume of timber (in m³) in the trunk of the tree.   (NEA; 1988)

Q8

A flat metal component is to be made in the shape shown in Fig. 10.62. The curves AB and DC are both arcs of circles with centre O. The radius of the arc AB is r, the radius of the arc DC is R. The angle AOB = 60°.

a) i) Write down a formula for the area of sector ODC in terms of R.

   ii) Show that the area of the shaded region ABCD is $\frac{1}{6}\pi(R^2-r^2)$.

The unshaded ends of the shape are both semi-circles.

b) i) Write down the length of the diameter BC in terms of R and r.
   ii) Find the total area of the two semi-circles in terms of R and r.
c) Find the area, in mm², to the nearest mm², of metal sheet required to make the component when OD = 39 mm and OA = 27 mm.   (LEAG; 1988)

Fig. 10.62

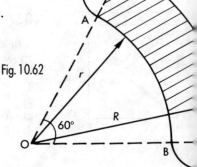

Q9

The box for a chocolate mint is a square-based pyramid with its point vertically above the middle of the base, as in Fig. 10.63. The sides of the base of the box are 6 cm long and the box is 6 cm tall.

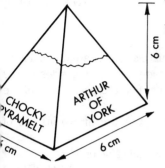

a) i) Calculate the diagonal distance across the base.
   ii) Calculate the length of a sloping edge.
b) Sketch a net for the box, indicating the lengths of the sides.

(WJEC; 1988)

Fig. 10.63

EXTENSION   **Q10**

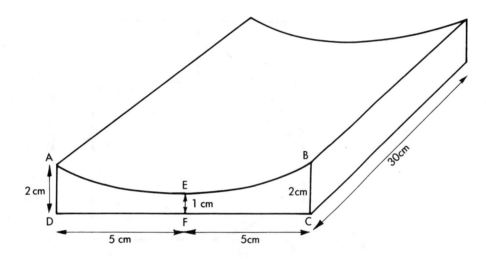

Fig. 10.64

Figure 10.64 shows a shallow glass dish of uniform cross-section. The dimensions of the cross-section ABCD are as shown in the diagram.

a) The curve AEB is the arc of a circle. Find the radius of the circle.
b) Given that the length of the dish is 30 cm and that the mass of 1 cm³ of glass is 2.45 g, find the mass of the dish.

(WJEC; 1988)

Q11

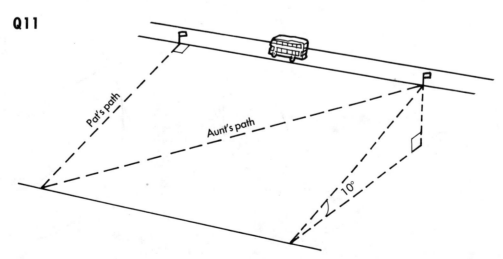

Fig. 10.65

A hillside slopes up at a steady 10° to the horizontal, as shown in Fig. 10.65. A horizontal road runs along the ridge at the top of the hill. Pat and her aunt want to walk up the hill to catch a bus which runs along the road. Pat takes the path which goes straight up the hill and

meets the road at right angles; but her aunt prefers a gentler path which climbs at only 5°
to the horizontal. Pat's path is 100 metres long. Calculate:

a) the height of the hill
b) the length of her aunt's path
c) the angle between their paths
d) how far apart they are when they reach the road.   (O and C; 1988)

Q12

a) Figure 10.66(a) shows a circle touching the sides of a square and a square drawn inside
    the circle with its vertices touching the circle at the mid-points of the sides of the
    outside square. Given that the radius of the circle is 1 cm find the perimeters of the
    two squares.
b) i) Figure 10.66(b) is like Fig 10.66(a), but regular octagons are drawn instead of
        squares. Find the perimeter of the two octagons.
    ii) What can you deduce from your results about the numerical value of π?
                                                                        (WJEC; 1988)

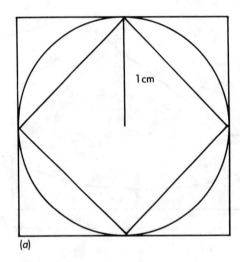
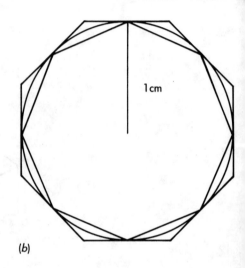

Fig. 10.66

(a)   (b)

Q13

a) In Fig. 10.67, AB is an arc of a circle, whose centre is at O. The radius is r, and the
    angle AOB is $x°$. Show that the length of the arc AB is given by the formula:

$$\text{arc length} = \frac{\pi}{180}\,xr.$$

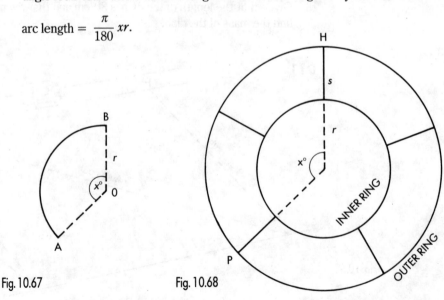

Fig. 10.67   Fig. 10.68

b) A housing estate has two circular roads with the same centre (the inner ring and the
    outer ring), with several radial roads joining them, as shown in Fig 10.68. The inner

ring has radius r metres, and the radial roads have length s metres, so that the outer ring has radius $(r+s)$ metres. My house H and the post office P are both on the outer ring, at the ends of radial roads. The angle between the radial roads leading to H and P is $x°$. Use the result in a) to write down formulas for the distance from H to P.

    i) if I go by the two radial roads and the inner ring,
    ii) if I go by the outer ring.

c)   If $x = 120$, which of the distances is greater? By how much? (The answer may involve r or s, or both.)

d)   Write down an equation if the two distances i) and ii) in b) are equal. Solve it to find x to the nearest whole number of degrees. What is surprising about the answer?

(O and C; 1988)

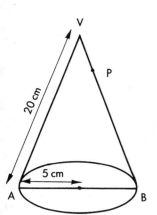

Fig. 10.69

Q14

Figure 10.69 shows a cone with circular base of radius 5 cm. The slant height of the cone is 20 cm. AB is a diameter of the base and V is the vertex of the cone. P is a point on VB such that VP:PB $= 1:3$. Find the shortest distance from A to P along the surface of the cone.

(WJEC)

OUTLINE ANSWERS TO EXAM QUESTIONS

A1

$\sin^{-1} 0.4567 = 27.2$, since $90 < x < 180$, then $x = 180-27.2 = 152.8°$.
(If you check this answer by finding sin 152.8, you will not get exactly 0.4567 since it is a rounded off answer.)

A2

a)   Radius is $(35-21)÷2 = 7$ cm.
b)   Total area is a complete circle of radius 7 cm, which is 153.9 cm².

A3

a)   Time $=$ distance$÷$speed, hence the time of the journey is 400 km divided by 320 km/h to give 1.25 hours, that is 1 hour 15 minutes. So from 2155, and on 1 hour 15 minutes to get to 2310, which is 'ten past eleven'.

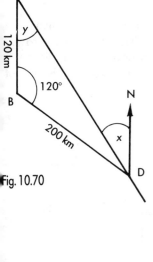

Fig. 10.70

b)   i) Since we have two sides and an included angle, we use the cosine rule to give
$$CD = \sqrt{(120^2+200^2-2\times120\times200\times\cos 120)} = 280 \text{ km.}$$
    ii) Bearing $= 360°-x°$ (see Fig. 10.70).
    $x° = y°$ (alternate angles).
    Hence find y and use the sine rule.

$$\frac{\sin y}{200} = \frac{\sin 120}{280} \rightarrow \sin y = \frac{200 \sin 120}{280}$$

$$\rightarrow y = 38.2°.$$

So the bearing of C from D is 322°.

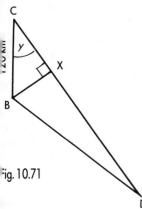

Fig. 10.71

    iii) The nearest distance will be the perpendicular from B to CD as shown Fig. 10.71.

$$\text{Hence } \frac{BX}{120} = \sin 38.2$$

$$BX = 120 \sin 38.2 = 74.2 \text{ km.}$$

A4

a)   BN $= 8 \sin 2.5° = 0.35$ km.

b)   AN $= 8 \cos 2.5 = 7.99$ km.

c)   By Pythagoras $CN^2 = AC^2 + AN^2 = 12^2 + 7.99^2$,
                 hence CN $= 14.42$ km.

d)   Tan (BCN) $= \dfrac{BN}{CN} = \dfrac{0.35}{14.42} = 0.0242$,

so the angle of elevation is $1.4°$.

A5

a) $100-x$

b) $\frac{1}{2} \times 100 \times (100-x) = 50(100-x) = 5000-50x$

c) $\dfrac{50}{2}(x+100) = 25x+2500$

d)   If area of trapezium = area of triangle then:
$$25x+2500 \quad = \quad 5000-50x$$
$$\rightarrow 25x+50x \quad = \quad 5000-2500$$
$$\rightarrow 75x \qquad\quad = \quad 2500$$
$$x \; = \; \dfrac{2500}{75} \; = \; 33\tfrac{1}{3} \text{ metres.}$$

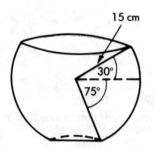

15 cm

Fig. 10.72

A6

a)   In Fig 10.72, arc length $= \dfrac{(30+75)}{360} \times \pi \times 2 \times 15 = 27.5$ cm.

b)   Latitude 30°N, longitude $\dfrac{360°}{3} = 120°E$.

c)   Latitude 0°, longitude $(120+180) = 300$ from E, which is longitude 60° W.

A7

i)   You should have sketched a shape like that in Fig 10.73. (You could perhaps make the horizontal distances more accurate by calculating the radius of the tree to be $68 \div 2\pi = 10.8$ cm $= 0.108$ m. Marks would not be lost whichever way you did it.)
Hence $x = 30 \tan 26 = 14.6$ m (14.7 if used the more accurate) so height of tree $= 14.6+1.2 = 15.8$ m (or 15.9 m).

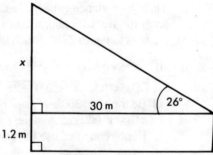

Fig. 10.73   1.2 m

ii) Use the formula for the volume of a cone,
$$V = \tfrac{1}{3}\pi r^2 h = \tfrac{1}{3} \times \pi \times (0.108)^2 \times 15.8 = 0.193 \text{ m}^3 \text{ (or 0.194 m}^3\text{)}.$$
This is one of those GCSE questions that allows you to estimate in your own way, and hence the choice of actual method and accuracy at the end. There is, of course, no 'correct' answer to this question, only acceptable ones.

A8

a)

i) $\dfrac{60}{360} \times \pi \times R^2 = \dfrac{1}{6}\pi R^2 = $ area of sector ODC.

ii) Area of sector OAB $= \dfrac{1}{6}\pi r^2.$

So, area of ABCD $= \dfrac{1}{6}\pi R^2 - \dfrac{1}{6}\pi r^2 = \dfrac{1}{6}\pi (R^2 - r^2).$

b) i) $R-r$

ii) $\pi\left(\dfrac{R-r}{2}\right)^2$ or $\dfrac{\pi}{4}(R-r)^2$.

c) Total area of the shape is given by $\dfrac{1}{6}\pi(R^2-r^2)+\dfrac{\pi}{4}(R-r)^2$.

When $R = 39$ mm and $r = 27$ mm then total area $=$

$\dfrac{1}{6}\times\pi\times 792 +\dfrac{\pi}{4}\times144 = 528$ mm^2.

A9

a) i) Use Pythagoras' theorem to give diagonal $= \sqrt{(6^2+6^2)} = 8.5$ cm.
   ii) Form a diagram as shown in Fig. 10.74, showing the right angled triangle formed with the perpendicular from the vertex to the centre of the base and the sloping edge. Using Pythagoras again to give,
   slope $= \sqrt{(6^2+4.25^2)}$ (4.25 being half of the diagonal)
   $= 7.3$ cm.

b) A net is shown in Fig 10.75, although this is not the only possible net for the pyramid.

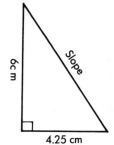

Fig. 10.74

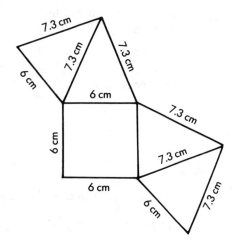

Fig. 10.75

A10

a) i) A helpful diagram here (see Fig 10.76) will help see us through the problem. Where O is the centre of the circle having the arc AEB, angle OEB is found by: tan E $= 5$
Hence OEB $= 78.7$
and OBE $\quad = 78.7$ (since OEB is isosceles).
Hence BOE $= 180-2\times78.7 = 22.6°$.

So radius OB is found by: $\dfrac{5}{r} = \sin 22.6$

$\rightarrow r = \dfrac{5}{\sin 22.6} = 13$ cm.

(It is helpful, and most accurate, to keep the angles found as accurately as you can in your calculator, and only write down the rounded off value as we did here.)

Fig. 10.76

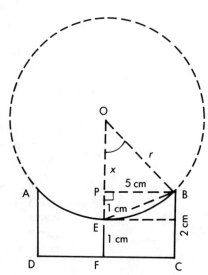

b) The area of the cross section of the dish EBCF is made up of a rectangle 5 cm², plus a triangle 2.5 cm² and minus the segment EB of the circle.

Area of segment EB = Area of sector OEB − Area of triangle OEB.

$$\text{Area of sector OEB} = \frac{22.6}{360} \times \pi \times 13^2 = 33.36$$

Area of triangle OEB = $\frac{1}{2} \times 13 \times 5 = 32.5$

Hence area of segment EB = 33.36 − 32.5 = 0.86 cm².

Hence area of cross section EFCB = (5 + 2.5 − 0.86) cm² = 6.64 cm².

Hence area of cross section ADFCBE = 2 × 6.64 = 13.28 cm².

Hence volume of dish = 13.28 × 30 = 398.4 cm³.

Hence mass of dish = 398.4 × 2.45 g = 976 g.

A11

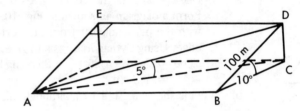

Fig. 10.77

Draw a diagram and fully label it as shown in Fig 10.77 to help you see the triangles involved.

a) Height DC given by DC = 100 sin 10° = 17.4 m.

b) Length AD given by $\dfrac{DC}{AD}$ = sin 5°,

hence AD = $\dfrac{DC}{\sin 5°} = \dfrac{17.4}{\sin 5°}$ = 199 m.

c) Angle EAD found by cos A = $\dfrac{AE}{AD} = \dfrac{100}{199}$ = 0.5019, hence angle = 60°.

d) Length ED given by AD sin A = 199 sin 60 = 172 m.

A12

a) Perimeter of large square = 4 × 2 cm = 8 cm. The length of the side of the smaller square is found by Pythagoras see Fig 10.78: if x is half the length, then $x^2 + x^2 = 1^2 \rightarrow 2x^2 = 1 \rightarrow x = \sqrt{(0.5)}$ = 0.71 cm. (Keep the accurate value in the calculator.) So the perimeter of the small square = 4 × 2 × 0.71 = 5.66 cm.

Fig. 10.78

b) i) Large octagon:
A simple sketch of part of the octagon, where O is the centre of the circle is drawn (see Fig 10.79).
Angle BOC = 360 ÷ 8 = 45°,
hence angle AOB = 45 ÷ 2 = 22.5°,

hence AB is found by $\dfrac{AB}{1}$ = tan 22.5.

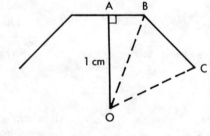

Fig. 10.79

So AB = 0.4142 and then the total perimeter of the large octagon = AB × 2 × 8 = 6.627 cm.

Small octagon:
A similar sketch (see Fig 10.80), but this time OB = 1 cm, angle AOB is still 22.5°, hence AB = 1 × sin 22.5 = 0.3827. Hence the total perimeter of the small octagon = AB × 2 × 8 = 6.123 cm.

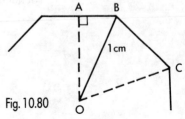

Fig. 10.80

ii) Since the value of the circumference of the circle lies between the perimeters of the octagons, then $6.123 <$ circumference < 6.627. The circumference of the circle is given by πD, so where $D = 2$ cm, circumference $= 2\pi$.
So in this situation we have:
$$6.123 < 2\pi < 6.627$$
$$\rightarrow 3.062 < \pi < 3.314.$$

A13

a) The arc length AB is directly proportional to the angle x, hence arc length $= Kx$. (K being a constant).
When $x = 360$, arc length $=$ circumference $= 2\pi r$,
hence $2\pi r = K.360$

$$\rightarrow \frac{2\pi r}{360} = K = \frac{\pi r}{180}$$

so arc length $= \frac{\pi r}{180} \times x = \frac{\pi}{180}xr.$

b) i) $s + \frac{\pi}{180}xr + s = 2s + \frac{\pi}{180}xr$

   ii) $\frac{\pi}{180}x(r+s).$

c) When $x = 120$ then i) $= 2s + \frac{\pi \times 120 \times r}{180} = 2s + \frac{2}{3}\pi r$

   ii) $= \frac{2}{3}\pi(r+s).$

Assume i) to be the largest value, then the difference is given by i)−ii)
$$= 2s + \frac{2}{3}\pi r - \frac{2}{3}\pi r - \frac{2}{3}\pi s = 2s - \frac{2}{3}\pi s$$

$$= 2s\left(1 - \frac{\pi}{3}\right) = -0.09s.$$

Since this value is negative, then i) must be the shortest route. So the greatest distance is given by the outer ring road by the length $0.09s$.

d) The two distances are equal when $2s + \frac{\pi xr}{180} = \frac{\pi xr}{180} + \frac{\pi xs}{180} \rightarrow 2s = \frac{\pi xs}{180}$

$$\rightarrow 360s = \pi xs$$
$$\rightarrow 360 = \pi x$$

$$\rightarrow x = \frac{360}{\pi} = 115°.$$

What is surprising is that this answer is totally independent of the lengths of r and s.

A14

Sketch a net of the cone to give a sector as in Fig. 10.81, with the dotted line AP being the shortest distance.
We need to find angle AVP, call it x.
Arc distance AB is half the circumference of the base of the cone, i.e. $\pi \times 5 = 5\pi$.
But from the circle with radius 20 cm,

arc length AB $= \frac{x}{360} \times \pi \times 2 \times 20 = \frac{40\pi x}{360}$

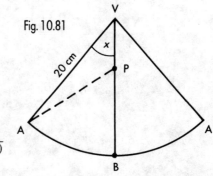
Fig. 10.81

hence $\frac{40\pi}{360}x = 5\pi \rightarrow x = \frac{5\pi \times 360}{40\pi} = 45.$

Since VP:PB $= 1:3$, then VP $= \frac{1}{4} \times 20 = 5$ cm.
Hence we can use the cosine rule to give
$$AP = \sqrt{(20^2 + 5^2 - 20 \times 5 \times \cos 45)} = \sqrt{(354.3)}$$
$$AP = 18.8 \text{ cm.}$$

TRANSFORMATION GEOMETRY

MATRICES

VECTORS

TRANSFORMATION MATRICES

INVERSE TRANSFORMATIONS

GETTING STARTED

It will be assumed in this chapter that you are familiar with the ideas of reflection, rotation, enlargement and translation, as the emphasis at this level will be matrix transformations as well as vector work. Do look carefully at the syllabus content in chapter 1, as this transformation work is not included in all syllabuses. However, at the higher level questions are always asked if it *is* in your syllabus.

USEFUL DEFINITIONS

Enlargement	A change in size to a mathematical similar shape (could be smaller).
Invariant	Does not alter under a transformation.
Invariant line	The line of points that will not alter under a transformation.
Invariant point	The point that will not alter under a transformation.
Matrix	A collection of numbers in some specific order.
Reflection	A mirror-image through a particular line.
Rotation	A turn around some particular point.
Transformation	A change of position of a given shape.
Translation	A slide with no turning.
Vector	A movement of a specific magnitude and direction.

ESSENTIAL PRINCIPLES

1 ⟩ MATRICES

A *matrix* is a collection of information in a specific order.

Eg. $\begin{pmatrix} 3 & 0 & 1 \\ 1 & 5 & 2 \end{pmatrix}$ is a 2 by 3 or (2×3) matrix, since it has 2 rows and 3 columns. This is called the *order* of the matrix.

ARITHMETIC

You may only add or subtract matrices with the same order, and then by combining corresponding positioned numbers.

Example: $\begin{pmatrix} 3 & 0 & 1 \\ 1 & 5 & 2 \end{pmatrix} + \begin{pmatrix} 4 & 2 & 7 \\ 0 & 1 & 3 \end{pmatrix} = \begin{pmatrix} 7 & 2 & 8 \\ 1 & 6 & 5 \end{pmatrix}$

To multiply two matrices you need first to consider their orders.

Example: Where $A = \begin{pmatrix} 1 & 2 & 3 & 4 \\ 5 & 6 & 7 & 8 \end{pmatrix}$ and $B = \begin{pmatrix} 0 & 3 & 7 \\ 9 & 1 & 0 \\ 2 & 6 & 3 \\ 5 & 4 & 6 \end{pmatrix}$

the order of A is (2×4) and the order of B is (4×3).

You can evaluate the product AB since (2×4)(4×3) has the middle two numbers the same, the end two numbers give the order of the answer, i.e. (2×3).

You then multiply the matrices by the 'diving board' technique (see Fig. 11.1).

'*Go along then down*'. Find the product of *EACH ROW* with *EACH COLUMN* starting at the top and right. The final product of a row with a column is by summing the individual products as you go along and down.

Fig. 11.1   'go along'   then   'down'

Example (see Fig. 11.2): To start multiplying A to B (i.e. AB) above, the first row in A and the first column in B, combining to give

$= (1 \times 0) + (2 \times 9) + (3 \times 2) + (4 \times 5)$
$= 0 + 18 + 6 + 20$
$= 44$

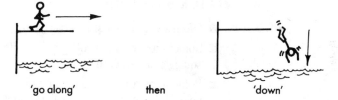

Fig. 11.2

since this is the product of first row with first column its position in the answer matrix is first row, first column. You can now check out yourself, by continuing this process, that

the final answer to AB is given by $\begin{pmatrix} 44 & 39 & 40 \\ 108 & 95 & 104 \end{pmatrix}$

If you then tried to evaluate BA, consider the orders (4×3)(2×4) you will see the middle two are not the same and so this product cannot be done.

Identity matrix

The identity matrix is the one that multiplies to any other and leaves it unaltered. It is $\begin{pmatrix} 1 & 0 \\ 0 & 1 \end{pmatrix}$.

Inverse matrices

A matrix and its inverse will multiply together to give the identity matrix.

This is a complicated formula and one of those always given on the formula sheet if you have it in your syllabus.

It is defined as:

$$\text{The inverse matrix of } \begin{pmatrix} a & b \\ c & d \end{pmatrix} \text{ is given by } \frac{1}{(ad-bc)} \begin{pmatrix} d & -b \\ -c & a \end{pmatrix}$$

The bracket $(ad-bc)$ is often referred to as the *determinant*. If the determinant of a matrix is zero, then there is no inverse of that matrix.

WORKED EXAMPLE 1

Find the inverse of the matrix $\begin{pmatrix} 4 & 1 \\ 3 & 2 \end{pmatrix}$.

Use the formula where $a = 4, b = 1, c = 3$ and $d = 2$

then the inverse is $\dfrac{1}{(4\times2-1\times3)} \begin{pmatrix} 2 & -1 \\ -3 & 4 \end{pmatrix} = \dfrac{1}{5}\begin{pmatrix} 2 & -1 \\ -3 & 4 \end{pmatrix} = \begin{pmatrix} 0.4 & -0.2 \\ -0.6 & 0.8 \end{pmatrix}$.

EXERCISE 1

Find the inverse of $\begin{pmatrix} 6 & 2 \\ 4 & 3 \end{pmatrix}$.

2 ⟩ VECTORS

A *vector* is a given displacement or movement. It has direction and a specific magnitude (size). Two vectors that are equal do not have to be in the same place, but they will be parallel.

VECTOR NOTATION

- Often a vector is just referred to by a bold small case letter, e.g. **a**.
- Sometimes because of printing difficulties you will find a vector written with a squiggle underneath as a.
- Sometimes a vector is defined on a diagram as being the vector from a point A to a point B, hence the vector can be labelled $\overrightarrow{AB}$ or $-\overrightarrow{BA}$.
- Vectors are often referred to as *column vectors*, as on the grid, by use of horizontal displacement and vertical displacement.

For example, in Fig. 11.3:

$$\mathbf{a} = \begin{pmatrix} 3 \\ 2 \end{pmatrix} \quad \mathbf{b} = \begin{pmatrix} 3 \\ -2 \end{pmatrix}$$

$$\overrightarrow{CD} = \begin{pmatrix} -2 \\ -2 \end{pmatrix}$$

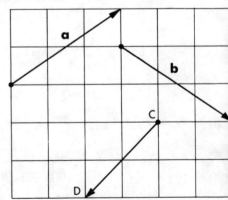

Fig. 11.3

VECTOR ADDITION AND SUBTRACTION

Look at Fig. 11.4 and note that $\mathbf{a}+\mathbf{b} = \mathbf{c}$. If you look at the 'column vectors', then

$$\text{where } \mathbf{a} = \begin{pmatrix} 1 \\ -2 \end{pmatrix} \quad \mathbf{b} = \begin{pmatrix} 2 \\ 3 \end{pmatrix}, \quad \mathbf{a}+\mathbf{b} = \begin{pmatrix} 1 \\ -2 \end{pmatrix}+\begin{pmatrix} 2 \\ 3 \end{pmatrix} = \begin{pmatrix} 3 \\ 1 \end{pmatrix}$$

which is **c**, hence illustrates $\mathbf{a}+\mathbf{b} = \mathbf{c}$

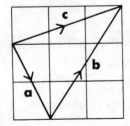

Fig. 11.4

This is often done wrong in examinations, look carefully at it.

Similarly if we looked at $\mathbf{a}-\mathbf{b} = \mathbf{d}$

then $\begin{pmatrix}1\\-2\end{pmatrix}-\begin{pmatrix}2\\3\end{pmatrix} = \begin{pmatrix}-1\\-5\end{pmatrix} = \mathbf{d}$

Notice on the grid in Fig. 11.5 how $-\mathbf{b}$ is the same size as $\mathbf{b}$ but the opposite direction.

Fig. 11.5

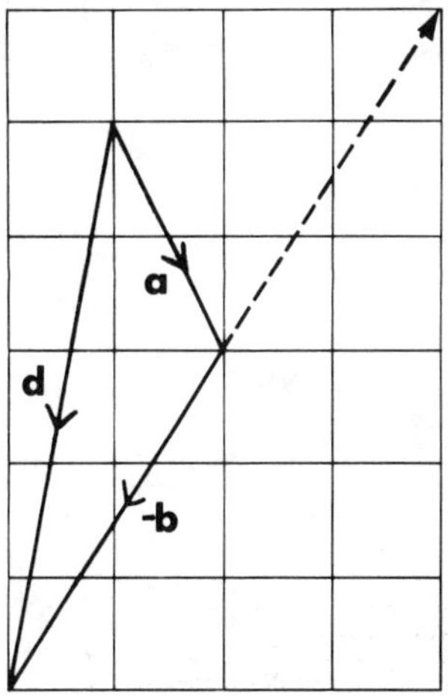

VECTOR MULTIPLICATION

Where $\mathbf{a} = \begin{pmatrix}3\\1\end{pmatrix}$ then $2\mathbf{a} = \begin{pmatrix}6\\2\end{pmatrix}$ etc.

$2\mathbf{a} = \mathbf{a}+\mathbf{a}$ (See Fig. 11.6).

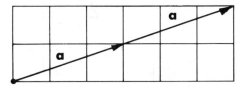

Fig. 11.6

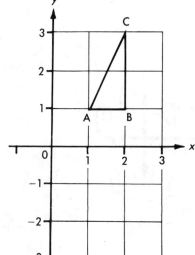

POSITION VECTORS

The *position vector* of any point A, is the vector from some given reference point (usually the origin) to that given point A. It follows that the position vector of the co-ordinate $(-1,3)$ will be $\begin{pmatrix}-1\\3\end{pmatrix}$.

MAGNITUDE

The *magnitude* of a vector can be represented by a length in a given diagram. The magnitude of any column vector can be found by Pythagoras' theorem.

So the magnitude of the vector $\begin{pmatrix}x\\y\end{pmatrix}$ is given by
$|\mathbf{a}| = \sqrt{(x^2+y^2)}$.
$|\mathbf{a}|$ is often used as notation for the magnitude of vector $\mathbf{a}$.

EXERCISE 2

Where $\mathbf{x} = \begin{pmatrix}3\\4\end{pmatrix}$ $\mathbf{y} = \begin{pmatrix}-4\\-1\end{pmatrix}$ $\mathbf{z} = \begin{pmatrix}2\\7\end{pmatrix}$

i) Calculate the magnitude of the vector $\mathbf{x}+\mathbf{y}$, i.e. $|\mathbf{x}+\mathbf{y}|$
ii) What is special about the vectors $\mathbf{x}+\mathbf{y}$ and $\mathbf{z}-\mathbf{x}$?

3 TRANSFORMATION MATRICES

A *transformation matrix* is usually a (2 by 2) matrix. If it is multiplied to a matrix containing the position vectors of any shape, then the resulting product will determine the transformed shape.

WORKED EXAMPLE 2

Exam questions are often phrased this way, do be familiar with it.

A transformation T is defined as

$$T: \begin{pmatrix}x\\y\end{pmatrix} \rightarrow \begin{pmatrix}1 & 0\\0 & -1\end{pmatrix}\begin{pmatrix}x\\y\end{pmatrix}$$

Fig. 11.7

Use this to transform the triangle in Fig. 11.7, then fully describe the transformation T. By putting the position vectors of the triangle ABC into a matrix we can evaluate

$$\begin{array}{ccc} & A\ B\ C & \quad A'\ B'\ C' \\ \begin{pmatrix} 1 & 0 \\ 0 & -1 \end{pmatrix} & \begin{pmatrix} 1 & 2 & 2 \\ 1 & 1 & 3 \end{pmatrix} = & \begin{pmatrix} 1 & 2 & 2 \\ -1 & -1 & -3 \end{pmatrix} \end{array}$$

Then plotting the transformed shape onto a diagram (see Fig. 11.8) gives us,

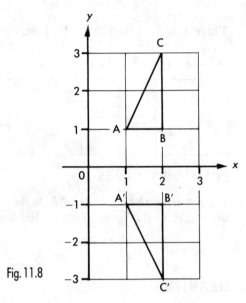

Fig. 11.8

which illustrates that T is a reflection in the X axis.

EXERCISE 3

By use of the triangle ABC in the worked example 1, fully describe transformations represented by the matrices

i) $\begin{pmatrix} 0 & 1 \\ 1 & 0 \end{pmatrix}$ ii) $\begin{pmatrix} 0 & -1 \\ 1 & 0 \end{pmatrix}$ iii) $\begin{pmatrix} 2 & 0 \\ 0 & 2 \end{pmatrix}$

BASE VECTORS

Base vectors, often called *unit vectors*, can be used to define very quickly a matrix transformation, or even to help evaluate that transformation. For example, where T:

$$T: \begin{pmatrix} x \\ y \end{pmatrix} \rightarrow \begin{pmatrix} 0 & -1 \\ -1 & 0 \end{pmatrix} \begin{pmatrix} x \\ y \end{pmatrix}$$

then consider how the unit matrix, $\begin{pmatrix} 1 & 0 \\ 0 & 1 \end{pmatrix}$ transforms to $\begin{pmatrix} 0 & -1 \\ -1 & 0 \end{pmatrix}$ where the columns of the matrices are position vectors.

Then it can be seen in Fig. 11.9 what happens to them.

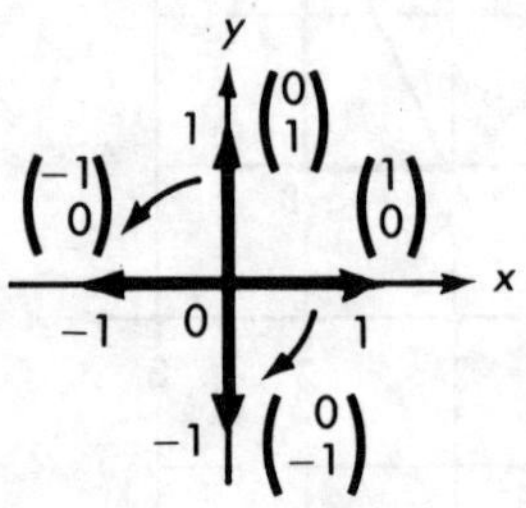

see that $\begin{pmatrix} 1 \\ 0 \end{pmatrix} \rightarrow \begin{pmatrix} 0 \\ -1 \end{pmatrix}$

$$\begin{pmatrix} 0 \\ 1 \end{pmatrix} \rightarrow \begin{pmatrix} -1 \\ 0 \end{pmatrix}$$

Fig. 11.9

The transformation can now be seen as "reflection in the line $y = -x$". Try this technique out on the matrices in Exercise 3 to see how much simpler it is to define the matrix in this way.

WORKED EXAMPLE 3

Find the transformation matrix that describes a rotation of 90° clockwise around the origin (see Fig. 11.10).
Consider the base vectors, then

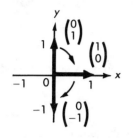

Fig. 11.10

$$\begin{pmatrix} 1 \\ 0 \end{pmatrix} \rightarrow \begin{pmatrix} 0 \\ -1 \end{pmatrix} \text{ and } \begin{pmatrix} 0 \\ 1 \end{pmatrix} \rightarrow \begin{pmatrix} 1 \\ 0 \end{pmatrix} \text{ (see Fig. 11.10)}$$

hence $\begin{pmatrix} 1 & 0 \\ 0 & 1 \end{pmatrix} \rightarrow \begin{pmatrix} 0 & 1 \\ -1 & 0 \end{pmatrix}$

so rotation of 90° clockwise around the origin is defined as

$$T: \begin{pmatrix} x \\ y \end{pmatrix} \rightarrow \begin{pmatrix} 0 & 1 \\ -1 & 0 \end{pmatrix} \begin{pmatrix} x \\ y \end{pmatrix}$$

EXERCISE 4

Find the transformation matrices that represent
i) enlargement of scale factor -3, centre of enlargement is the origin
ii) rotation of 180° around the origin

COMBINATIONS OF TRANSFORMATIONS

Two or more matrices can quite easily be combined by finding the product of their transformation matrices.

WORKED EXAMPLE 4

A transformation is defined as "reflect in the Y axis, then rotate through 90° anti-clockwise (around the origin)". What single transformation will this represent?
Find the transformation matrix for each transformation.

Reflect in Y axis (see Fig. 11.11):

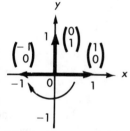

ig. 11.11

$$\begin{pmatrix} 1 \\ 0 \end{pmatrix} \rightarrow \begin{pmatrix} -1 \\ 0 \end{pmatrix} \text{ and } \begin{pmatrix} 0 \\ 1 \end{pmatrix} \rightarrow \begin{pmatrix} 0 \\ 1 \end{pmatrix}$$

hence $\begin{pmatrix} 1 & 0 \\ 0 & 1 \end{pmatrix} \rightarrow \begin{pmatrix} -1 & 0 \\ 0 & 1 \end{pmatrix}$

Rotate anticlockwise 90° (see Fig. 11.12):

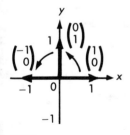

g. 11.12

$$\begin{pmatrix} 1 \\ 0 \end{pmatrix} \rightarrow \begin{pmatrix} 0 \\ 1 \end{pmatrix} \text{ and } \begin{pmatrix} 0 \\ 1 \end{pmatrix} \rightarrow \begin{pmatrix} -1 \\ 0 \end{pmatrix}$$

hence $\begin{pmatrix} 1 & 0 \\ 0 & 1 \end{pmatrix} \rightarrow \begin{pmatrix} 0 & -1 \\ 1 & 0 \end{pmatrix}$

Hence the *combined* transformation will be:

$$\begin{pmatrix} x \\ y \end{pmatrix} \rightarrow \begin{pmatrix} 0 & -1 \\ 1 & 0 \end{pmatrix} \begin{pmatrix} -1 & 0 \\ 0 & 1 \end{pmatrix} \begin{pmatrix} x \\ y \end{pmatrix}$$

(note how the first transformation performed needs to be on the right),

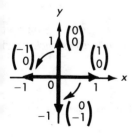

g. 11.13

i.e. $\begin{pmatrix} x \\ y \end{pmatrix} \rightarrow \begin{pmatrix} 0 & -1 \\ -1 & 0 \end{pmatrix} \begin{pmatrix} x \\ y \end{pmatrix}$

which is $\begin{pmatrix} 1 \\ 0 \end{pmatrix} \rightarrow \begin{pmatrix} 0 \\ -1 \end{pmatrix}$ and $\begin{pmatrix} 0 \\ 1 \end{pmatrix} \rightarrow \begin{pmatrix} -1 \\ 0 \end{pmatrix}$

seen as Fig. 11.13. Hence a relfection in the line $y = -x$.

Remember, give the answer as a single transformation. It's wrong if you state two transformations.

EXERCISE 5

Find the combination of the transformations:

i) rotate 90° clockwise around the origin then reflect in the x axis.

ii) reflect in the x axis and then rotate 90° clockwise around the origin.

4   INVERSE TRANSFORMATIONS

The *inverse* of a transformation is that transformation which moves a shape back to where it started. For example:

the inverse of "rotation of 90° clockwise around the origin" is . . .

a "rotation of 90° anticlockwise around the origin."

Or, the inverse of "an enlargement of scale factor 3, centre of enlargement (0,0)", is an enlargement of scale factor $\frac{1}{3}$, centre of enlargement (0,0)". *Self inverses* are those that are the inverses of themselves; all reflections are self inverses. For example, the inverse of

"reflection in the x-axis" is "reflection in the x-axis".

The matrix representing the inverse of a transformation T, will be the inverse matrix of the matrix representing T.

WORKED EXAMPLE 5

Find the matrix defining the inverse of the transformation T, where

$$T: \begin{pmatrix} x \\ y \end{pmatrix} \rightarrow \begin{pmatrix} 2 & 3 \\ 1 & 2 \end{pmatrix} \begin{pmatrix} x \\ y \end{pmatrix},$$ and hence find the point P that has the image under T of (3,1).

Inverse matrix of $\begin{pmatrix} 2 & 3 \\ 1 & 2 \end{pmatrix}$ is given by $\dfrac{1}{ad-bc} \begin{pmatrix} d & -b \\ -c & a \end{pmatrix}$

where $a = 2, b = 3, c = 1$ and $d = 2$.

Hence inverse matrix is $\dfrac{1}{(4-3)} \begin{pmatrix} 2 & -3 \\ -1 & 2 \end{pmatrix} = \begin{pmatrix} 2 & -3 \\ -1 & 2 \end{pmatrix}$

So the point P will be $\begin{pmatrix} 2 & -3 \\ -1 & 2 \end{pmatrix} \begin{pmatrix} 3 \\ 1 \end{pmatrix} = \begin{pmatrix} 3 \\ -1 \end{pmatrix}$

INVARIANCE

Most transformations have a point or a line of points that do not alter under the transformation. These are called 'invariant points' or the 'invariant line'. For example: in the transformation 'rotation of 90° clockwise about (0,0)' the point (0,0) is the invariant point (see Fig 11.14).

NB. The centre of rotation will always be the point of invariance of a rotation.

As in any reflection, the line of reflection is the invariant line.

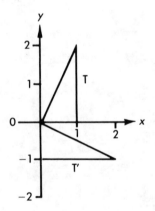

Fig. 11.14

EXERCISE 6

Write down the invariant point(s) of the transformations represented by:

i) $\begin{pmatrix} 0 & -1 \\ -1 & 0 \end{pmatrix}$ ii) $\begin{pmatrix} 2 & 0 \\ 0 & 1 \end{pmatrix}$

FURTHER TRANSFORMATIONS

There are a number of transformations that are only likely to be examined at the highest level of GCSE mathematics (if they are on your syllabus). These are *one way stretches* and *shears*.

One-way stretch

A *one way stretch* is an enlargement in one direction only. The transformation matrix of a one way stretch is of the type:

$\begin{pmatrix} K & 0 \\ 0 & 1 \end{pmatrix}$: a one way stretch of scale factor K with y axis invariant.

$$\begin{pmatrix} 1 & 0 \\ 0 & K \end{pmatrix} : \text{a one way stretch of scale factor K with } x \text{ axis invariant.}$$

Shear

A *shear* is a 'push over'. It has an invariant line and any point, P, moves in a direction parallel to the invariant line, and a distance of (perpendicular distance from the invariant line) multiplied by the (shear factor).

WORKED EXAMPLE 6

On the diagram in Fig. 11.15, construct the image of A′B′C′ of ABC under the shear which has invariant line *l* and maps A onto A′.

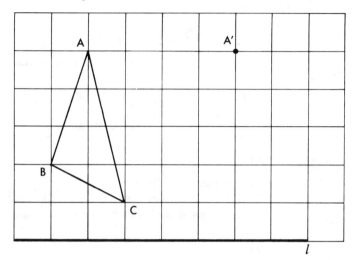

Fig. 11.15

As the shear is a 'push over' with *l* invariant, draw the lines from A through each of the points B and C to the invariant points, X and Y respectively. Then from X and Y draw in the 'push over' to XA′ and YA′. Each point moves parallel to the invariant line, hence follow B and C along their lines of parallel to the lines XA′ and YA′ respectively to find B′ and C′.

Hence join up A′B′C′ as in Fig. 11.16. (The shear factor here is $\frac{4}{5}$, since point A, 5 units from the invariant line, has only moved 4 units.)

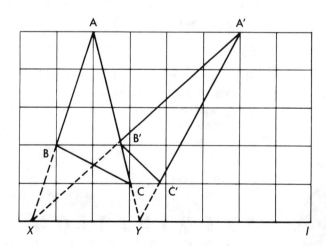

Fig. 11.16

SOLUTIONS TO EXERCISES

S1

$$\frac{1}{10}\begin{pmatrix} 3 & -2 \\ -4 & 6 \end{pmatrix}$$

S2

i) $\mathbf{x+y} = \begin{pmatrix} 3+-4 \\ 4+-1 \end{pmatrix} = \begin{pmatrix} -1 \\ 3 \end{pmatrix}$

magnitude $= \sqrt{((-1)^2+3^2)} = \sqrt{(10)} = 3.2$

ii) $\mathbf{z-x} = \begin{pmatrix} 2-3 \\ 7-4 \end{pmatrix} = \begin{pmatrix} -1 \\ 3 \end{pmatrix}$ which is equal to $\mathbf{x+y}$.

The vectors $(\mathbf{x+y})$ and $(\mathbf{z-x})$ are equal.

S3

i) reflection in the line $y = x$
ii) rotation of $90°$ anticlockwise around the origin.
iii) enlargement, scale factor 2, centre of enlargement the origin.

S4

i) $\begin{pmatrix} -3 & 0 \\ 0 & -3 \end{pmatrix}$ ii) $\begin{pmatrix} -1 & 0 \\ 0 & -1 \end{pmatrix}$

S5

i) combine the two transformations with base vectors or otherwise to give a 'reflection in the line $y = x$'.
ii) reflection in the line $y = -x$.

(Note that when you combine transformations in different orders, you usually get a different result.)

S6

i) the matrix can be seen to represent a reflection in the line $y = -x$, which is the invariant line.
ii) try out the transformation to see that it 'stretches' out from the y axis, which is the invariant line.

EXAMINATION TYPE QUESTIONS

Q1

In a video game in Fig. 11.17, the screen is 100 units by 100 units. The player has to enter a vector to give the direction the ball will travel. The ball starts at O(0,0). John enters the vector $\begin{pmatrix} 1 \\ 2 \end{pmatrix}$ and the ball moves, making an angle $a°$ with OR.

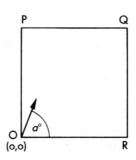

Fig. 11.17

a) What is the value of a?
b) The position of the ball as it moves to the top of the screen, PQ, can be written as

$K\begin{pmatrix}1\\2\end{pmatrix}$. What is the value of K when the ball reaches PQ?

c) What are the co-ordinates of the point where the ball hits PQ?
d) When the ball hits PQ it rebounds so that the 'new' path is at 90° to the 'old' path. Which vector describes the ball's direction after it rebounds from PQ?
e) What are the co-ordinates of the point where the ball hits QR? (WJEC; 1988)

Q2

On the isometric grid in Fig. 11.18, $\overrightarrow{OA}$ and $\overrightarrow{OB}$ represent **a** and **b** respectively.

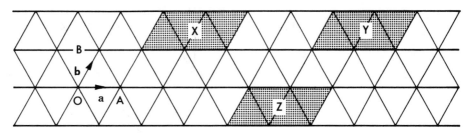

Fig. 11.18

Express, in terms of **a** and **b**, the translation which maps

a) shape X onto shape Y.
b) shape X onto shape Z. (NEA; 1988)

Q3

Transformation A is "reflect in the line $y = x$," followed by the translation $\begin{pmatrix}-1\\1\end{pmatrix}$.

Transformation B is "reflect in the line $x+y = 0$."

a) On graph paper, using a scale of 2 cm to 1 unit on each axis,
i) draw the triangle, T, with corners at (0,0), (2,0) and (2,1),
ii) draw the image of T under A. Label it T'.
b) Draw the image of T' under B. Label it T".
c) T may be mapped directly onto T" by the transformation C:

"half-turn about point W, followed by a translation $\begin{pmatrix}p\\q\end{pmatrix}$".

Find the co-ordinates of W and the vector $\begin{pmatrix}p\\q\end{pmatrix}$. (LEAG; 1988)

Q4

OPQR is a parallelogram. The vectors **x** and **y** are such that

$\overrightarrow{OP} = \mathbf{x+y}$ and $\overrightarrow{OR} = \mathbf{x-y}$.

a) Express, as simply as possible, in terms of x and/or **y**

i) $\overrightarrow{OQ}$; ii) $\overrightarrow{RP}$
b) What special type of parallelogram is OPQR
i) when $|\mathbf{x+y}| = |\mathbf{x-y}|$?
ii) when $|\mathbf{x}| = |\mathbf{y}|$? (MEG; 1988)

> **❝❝Remember base vectors, but do explain what you've done.❞❞**

Q5

A transformation, T, consists of a 90° anti-clockwise rotation about the origin (0,0), followed by a translation of $\begin{pmatrix} 6 \\ 4 \end{pmatrix}$.

a) Work out and write down the matrix which represents a 90° anti-clockwise rotation about the origin (0,0).

b) AB is a line segment with co-ordinates A(1,2) and B(2,4). Find the image of this line segment AB under the transformation T. Draw both AB and its image on a suitable pair of axes.

c) There is one point (called the invariant point) which remains in its original position under the transformation T. Find the co-ordinates of this point.

d) The transformation T is equivalent to a single rotation. State the centre and the angle of the rotation.   (NEA; 1988)

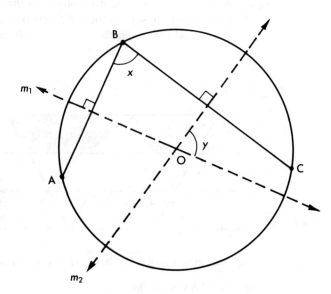

Fig. 11.19

Q6

In Fig. 11.19, A, B and C are three points on the circumference of a circle with centre O. The diameters at right-angles to AB and BC are m_1 and m_2 respectively. M_1 and M_2 are the transformations "reflect in m_1" and "reflect in m_2" respectively.

a) Identify $M_1(A)$, the image of A under the transformation M_1.

b) Identify i) $M_2(B)$; ii) $M_2M_1(A)$.

c) Explain why, in the figure, the angles marked x and y are equal.

d) Describe fully the single transformation equivalent to M_2M_1 and hence express angle AOC in terms of y.

e) Comment on the relationship between the angles AOC and ABC.   (MEG; 1988)

Q7

The matrix M is defined as M $= \begin{pmatrix} -1 & 3 \\ -1 & 1 \end{pmatrix}$

a) Calculate M^2.

The triangle T has vertices A(1,1), B(4,1) and C(1,2).

b) Find the co-ordinates of the vertices of T_1, the image of T under the transformation whose matrix is M^2.

c) Using graph paper and taking a scale of 1 cm to 1 unit on each axis, draw and label the triangles T and T_1.

d) Describe fully, in words, the single transformation which maps T onto T_1.   (LEAG; 1988)

Q8

Look at Fig. 11.20.

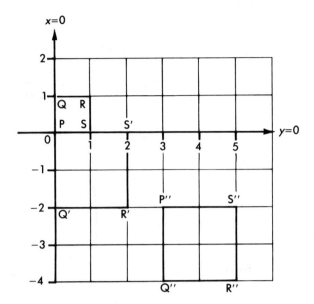

Fig. 11.20

a) Describe *two* successive transformations which will map the unit square PQRS onto the square PQ′R′S′.
b) Hence, or otherwise, give the transformation matrix which will map the square PQRS onto the square PQ′R′S.
c) A transformation T which maps the unit square PQRS onto the square P″Q″R″S″ is given by $\begin{pmatrix} x \\ y \end{pmatrix} \rightarrow \begin{pmatrix} ax+b \\ cy+d \end{pmatrix}$

By using the result obtained in part b), or otherwise, find the values of a, b, c and d.

d) What transformation matrix will map the square PQ′R′S′ onto the square PQRS?

(NEA; 1988)

Q9

In Fig. 11.21, OABC is a plane quadrilateral with $\overrightarrow{OA} = 4\mathbf{a}$, $\overrightarrow{OB} = 2\mathbf{a}+2\mathbf{c}$, $\overrightarrow{OC} = 3\mathbf{c}$.

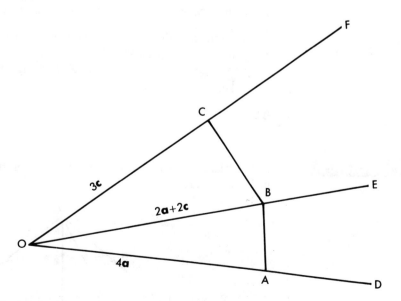

Fig. 11.21

a) Express the vectors $\overrightarrow{CO}$, $\overrightarrow{CB}$ and $\overrightarrow{AB}$ in terms of **a** or **c** or **a** and **c**.

   The lines OA, OB and OC are produced to D, E and F respectively, where OC = CF and OB : BE = OA : AD = 2 : 1.

b) Find $\overrightarrow{FC}$, $\overrightarrow{FE}$ and $\overrightarrow{DE}$ in terms of **a** or **c** or **a** and **c**.

c) Write down two geometrical facts about the points D, E and F.   (LEAG; 1988)

Q10

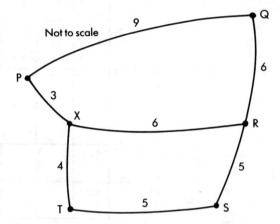

Fig. 11.22

The map in Fig. 11.22 shows the main roads between five villages, P, Q, R, S and T, X is merely a road junction. The numbers on the map are distances in kilometres.

   A wholesaler wishes to site his warehouse so that he can best serve the small shops in each village. The wholesaler takes the goods to the shops visiting a different village each day.

a) Complete the matrix **D** in Fig. 11.23 which shows the least road distance between any pair of villages.

$$
\mathbf{D} = \begin{array}{c} \\ P \\ Q \\ R \\ S \\ T \end{array}
\begin{array}{c} \begin{matrix} P & Q & R & S & T \end{matrix} \\
\left[\begin{matrix}
0 & 9 & 9 & 12 & 7 \\
9 & 0 & 6 & 11 & 16 \\
 & & & & \\
 & & & & \\
 & & & & \\
\end{matrix}\right] \end{array}
$$

Fig. 11.23

b) The running costs for the wholesaler depend on both the bulk of goods to be transported and the distance to be travelled. He therefore considers the product of distance and population (assuming that bulk of goods is proportional to the population). The matrix, **N**, of populations (in hundreds) is shown in Fig. 11.24.

   Form the matrix **DN** and, on the basis of your result, advise the wholesaler in which village he should place his warehouse.

c) A suitable site becomes available at X. Investigate whether the wholesaler should be advised to take this site.   (MEG; 1988)

$$
\mathbf{N} = \begin{array}{c} P \\ Q \\ R \\ S \\ T \end{array}
\left[\begin{matrix}
12 \\
16 \\
7 \\
6 \\
20
\end{matrix}\right]
$$

Fig. 11.24

Q11

EXTENSION

In the triangle OAB shown in Fig. 11.25, T is the mid-point of AB, and M is the mid-point of AT.

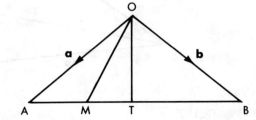

Fig. 11.25

a) Given that $\overrightarrow{OA}$ = **a** and $\overrightarrow{OB}$ = **b**, express as simply as possible in terms of **a** and/or **b**:

   i) $\overrightarrow{AM}$; ii) $\overrightarrow{OM}$.

b) Given that **a** = $\begin{pmatrix} 5 \\ 3 \end{pmatrix}$ and $\overrightarrow{AB}$ = $\begin{pmatrix} -2 \\ 1 \end{pmatrix}$ find:

   i) the co-ordinates of B

   ii) $|\overrightarrow{AB}|$
   iii) the co-ordinates of a point R such that $\overrightarrow{OR}$ = $\overrightarrow{BA}$.

c) Given that **s** = $\begin{pmatrix} 1 \\ 1 \end{pmatrix}$ and **u** = $\begin{pmatrix} 8 \\ 2 \end{pmatrix}$ and that $k\mathbf{a}+l\mathbf{s}$ = **u** then find the values of k and l.

OUTLINE ANSWERS TO EXAM QUESTIONS

A1

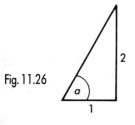

Fig. 11.26

a) a = $\tan^{-1}\dfrac{2}{1}$, giving a = 63.4°. See Fig. 11.26

b) At the top of the screen, the y ordinate will be 100, hence K will be 50 as 2×50 = 100.

c) $50\begin{pmatrix} 1 \\ 2 \end{pmatrix}$ = $\begin{pmatrix} 50 \\ 100 \end{pmatrix}$, hence co-ordinate is (50,100).

Fig. 11.27

d) As in Fig. 11.27, the vector perpendicular to $\begin{pmatrix} 1 \\ 2 \end{pmatrix}$ will be $\begin{pmatrix} 2 \\ -1 \end{pmatrix}$.

e) The ball needs to go 50 units to the right, hence the ball will move $25\begin{pmatrix} 2 \\ -1 \end{pmatrix}$ = $\begin{pmatrix} 50 \\ -25 \end{pmatrix}$.

   25 units down from the top is 75 on the y axis, and QR is x = 100, so the co-ordinate where QR is hit is (100,75).

A2

a) Count how many moves equivalent to **a each** point takes, and this is 4, hence the translation is given by 4**a**.
b) $3\mathbf{a}-2\mathbf{b}$. Notice how to move down the grid you need to use $-\mathbf{b}$.

A3

a), b), c). Your solution should be as in Fig. 11.28.

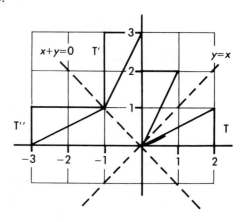

Fig. 11.28

d) There are many different possible answers here, some of which are:

half turn about (0,0) followed by $\begin{pmatrix} -1 \\ 1 \end{pmatrix}$

or half turn about (2,1) followed by $\begin{pmatrix} -5 \\ -1 \end{pmatrix}$

or half turn about $(-\frac{1}{2}, \frac{1}{2})$ followed by $\begin{pmatrix} 0 \\ 0 \end{pmatrix}$!!

Could your solution be one of these above?

A4

a) Find your parallelogram from the vectors **x** and **y**, as in Fig. 11.29:

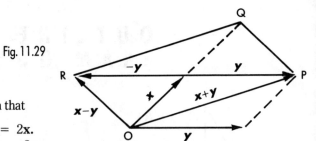

Fig. 11.29

Then it can clearly be seen that

i) $\overrightarrow{OQ} = \mathbf{x}+\mathbf{y}+(\mathbf{x}-\mathbf{y}) = 2\mathbf{x}$.
ii) $\overrightarrow{RP} = (\mathbf{x}+\mathbf{y})-(\mathbf{x}-\mathbf{y}) = 2\mathbf{y}$.

b) When $|\mathbf{x}+\mathbf{y}| = |\mathbf{x}-\mathbf{y}|$ then the sides of the parallelogram OPQR are equal, hence it is a rhombus.

c) When $|\mathbf{x}| = |\mathbf{y}|$, then the diagonals RP and OQ, given by $2\mathbf{x}$ and $2\mathbf{y}$ respectively, will be the same length, hence it will be a rectangle.

A5

a) Consider base vectors as in Fig. 11.30:

$$\begin{pmatrix} 1 \\ 0 \end{pmatrix} \to \begin{pmatrix} 0 \\ 1 \end{pmatrix} \text{ and } \begin{pmatrix} 0 \\ 1 \end{pmatrix} \to \begin{pmatrix} -1 \\ 0 \end{pmatrix}$$

hence $\begin{pmatrix} 1 & 0 \\ 0 & 1 \end{pmatrix} \to \begin{pmatrix} 0 & -1 \\ 1 & 0 \end{pmatrix}$

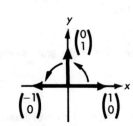

Fig. 11.30

so the transformation matrix will be $\begin{pmatrix} 0 & -1 \\ 1 & 0 \end{pmatrix}$

b) You should have a diagram as in Fig. 11.31.
    The dotted AB being the first rotation of 90° anticlockwise.

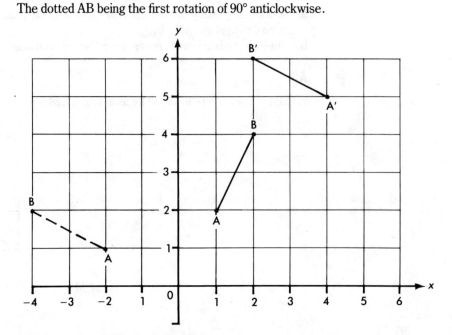

Fig. 11.31

c) If we define the transformation as T: $\begin{pmatrix} x \\ y \end{pmatrix} \rightarrow \begin{pmatrix} 0 & -1 \\ 1 & 0 \end{pmatrix}\begin{pmatrix} x \\ y \end{pmatrix} + \begin{pmatrix} 6 \\ 4 \end{pmatrix}$

then we obtain $\begin{pmatrix} x \\ y \end{pmatrix} \rightarrow \begin{pmatrix} -y \\ x \end{pmatrix} + \begin{pmatrix} 6 \\ 4 \end{pmatrix}$

So for the invariant point $x = -y+6 \rightarrow x+y = 6$

and $y = x+4 \rightarrow -x+y = 4$

Solving these two simultaneous equations we get: $y = 5$ and $x = 1$, hence the invariant point is (1,5).

d) The centre of rotation is the invariant point (1,5). Since the lines AB and A′B′ are perpendicular, we just need to look at how the line AB will rotate around (1,5) to give A′B′, and we see it is an anti-clockwise rotation of 90°.

A6

a) $M_1(A)$ will be point B.

b) i) $M_2(B)$ will be point C; ii) $M_2M_1(A)$ will be point C.

c) Sketch the shape as in Fig. 11.32 and label the midpoints of AB and BC, P and Q respectively. Then since angles BPO and BQO are 90° each, $x+QOP = 180°$ and $y+QOP = 180°$. Hence $x = y$.

d) The combination of two reflections always gives a rotation with centre of rotation the point of intersection of both lines of reflection, with the angle of rotation double the size of the angle both lines of reflection make.

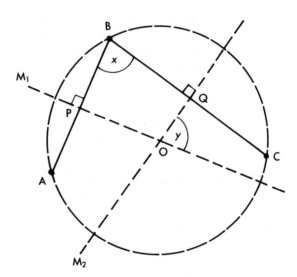

Fig. 11.32

So here the transformation is a rotation, centre of rotation O, through an angle of $2y$. Hence AOC $= 2y$.

e) AOC is double the size of ABC.

A7

a) $M^2 = \begin{pmatrix} -1 & 3 \\ -1 & 1 \end{pmatrix}\begin{pmatrix} -1 & 3 \\ -1 & 1 \end{pmatrix} = \begin{pmatrix} -2 & 0 \\ 0 & -2 \end{pmatrix}$

b) $\begin{pmatrix} -2 & 0 \\ 0 & -2 \end{pmatrix}\begin{pmatrix} 1 & 4 & 1 \\ 1 & 1 & 2 \end{pmatrix} = \begin{pmatrix} -2 & -8 & -2 \\ -2 & -2 & -4 \end{pmatrix}$

Hence the images of A, B and C respectively are $(-2, -2)$, $(-8, -2)$ and $(-2, -4)$.

c) See Fig. 11.33.

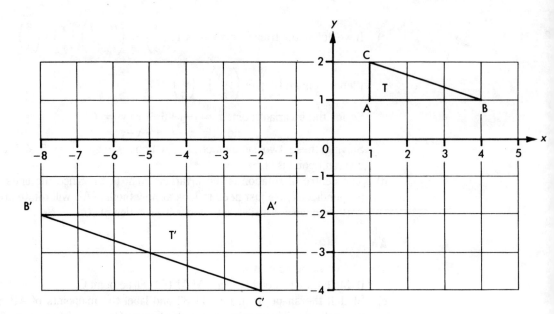

Fig. 11.33

d) An enlargement, scale factor -2, centre of enlargement the origin.

A8

a) Reflection in the x-axis followed by enlargement of scale factor 2, centre of enlargement the origin. (Or the other way round.) (There are more obtuse ways, but none so simple as the above.)

b) Look at base vectors, and see that $\begin{pmatrix} 1 \\ 0 \end{pmatrix} \rightarrow \begin{pmatrix} 2 \\ 0 \end{pmatrix}$ and $\begin{pmatrix} 0 \\ 1 \end{pmatrix} \rightarrow \begin{pmatrix} 0 \\ -2 \end{pmatrix}$

Hence $\begin{pmatrix} 1 & 0 \\ 0 & 1 \end{pmatrix} \rightarrow \begin{pmatrix} 2 & 0 \\ 0 & -2 \end{pmatrix}$ the matrix.

c) T can also be written as T: $\begin{pmatrix} x \\ y \end{pmatrix} \rightarrow \begin{pmatrix} 2 & 0 \\ 0 & -2 \end{pmatrix} \begin{pmatrix} x \\ y \end{pmatrix} + \begin{pmatrix} 3 \\ -2 \end{pmatrix}$

Hence $\begin{pmatrix} 2 & 0 \\ 0 & -2 \end{pmatrix} \begin{pmatrix} x \\ y \end{pmatrix} + \begin{pmatrix} 3 \\ -2 \end{pmatrix} = \begin{pmatrix} ax+b \\ cx+d \end{pmatrix}$

$\rightarrow \begin{pmatrix} 2x+3 \\ -2y-2 \end{pmatrix} = \begin{pmatrix} ax+b \\ cx+d \end{pmatrix} \rightarrow \begin{matrix} a = 2 \text{ and } b = 3 \\ c = -2 \text{ and } d = -2 \end{matrix}$

d) The answer is the inverse matrix of $\begin{pmatrix} 2 & 0 \\ 0 & -2 \end{pmatrix} = \dfrac{1}{-4} \begin{pmatrix} -2 & 0 \\ 0 & 2 \end{pmatrix} = \begin{pmatrix} \frac{1}{2} & 0 \\ 0 & -\frac{1}{2} \end{pmatrix}$

A9

a) $\overrightarrow{CO} = -3\mathbf{c}, \ \overrightarrow{CB} = -3\mathbf{c} + (2\mathbf{a}+2\mathbf{c}) = 2\mathbf{a}-\mathbf{c}$

$\overrightarrow{AB} = -4\mathbf{a} + 2\mathbf{a} + 2\mathbf{c} = 2\mathbf{c} - 2\mathbf{a}$

b) $\overrightarrow{FC} = -3\mathbf{c}, \ \overrightarrow{BE} = \frac{1}{2}(2\mathbf{a}+2\mathbf{c}) = \mathbf{a}+\mathbf{c}$

$\overrightarrow{FE} = -6\mathbf{c} + (3\mathbf{a}+3\mathbf{c}) = 3\mathbf{a}-3\mathbf{c}$

$\overrightarrow{DE} = -6\mathbf{a} + (3\mathbf{a}+3\mathbf{c}) = 3\mathbf{c}-3\mathbf{a}$

c) $\overrightarrow{FE} = 3\mathbf{a}-3\mathbf{c} \text{ and } \overrightarrow{DE} = -3\mathbf{a}+3\mathbf{c} = -(3\mathbf{a}-3\mathbf{c})$

Hence $\overrightarrow{FE} = -\overrightarrow{DE}$ or rather $\overrightarrow{FE} = \overrightarrow{ED}$.
Hence we see that F, E and D are co-linear (all in the same straight line) and that E is exactly halfway between F and D.

A10

a) See Fig. 11.34

$$\mathbf{D} = \begin{array}{c} \\ P \\ Q \\ R \\ S \\ T \end{array} \begin{array}{c} \begin{array}{ccccc} P & Q & R & S & T \end{array} \\ \begin{bmatrix} 0 & 9 & 9 & 12 & 7 \\ 9 & 0 & 6 & 11 & 16 \\ 9 & 6 & 0 & 5 & 10 \\ 12 & 11 & 5 & 0 & 5 \\ 7 & 16 & 10 & 5 & 0 \end{bmatrix} \end{array}$$

Fig. 11.34

b) See Fig. 11.35

$$\begin{bmatrix} 0 & 9 & 9 & 12 & 7 \\ 9 & 0 & 6 & 11 & 16 \\ 9 & 6 & 0 & 5 & 10 \\ 12 & 11 & 5 & 0 & 5 \\ 7 & 16 & 10 & 5 & 0 \end{bmatrix} \begin{bmatrix} 12 \\ 16 \\ 7 \\ 6 \\ 20 \end{bmatrix} = \begin{bmatrix} 419 \\ 536 \\ 434 \\ 455 \\ 440 \end{bmatrix}$$

Fig. 11.35

The product matrix gives the running costs for the warehouse at P, Q, R, S and T respectively. Hence P is the cheapest at 419.

If a site is available at X, then the distances to each P, Q, R, S and T is given by (3, 12, 6, 9, 4), hence running costs are proportional to the product of this matrix and **N** (see Fig. 11.36), which is less than 434 the previous lowest. So, yes, the wholesaler should be advised to take this site.

$$\begin{pmatrix} 3 & 12 & 6 & 9 & 4 \end{pmatrix} \begin{pmatrix} 12 \\ 16 \\ 7 \\ 6 \\ 20 \end{pmatrix} = 404$$

Fig. 11.36

A11

a)
i) $\overrightarrow{AM} = \frac{1}{4}\overrightarrow{AB}$, and $\overrightarrow{AB} = \mathbf{b}-\mathbf{a}$, hence $\overrightarrow{AM} = \frac{1}{4}(\mathbf{b}-\mathbf{a})$.
ii) $\overrightarrow{OM} = \mathbf{a}+\overrightarrow{AM} = \mathbf{a}+\frac{1}{4}(\mathbf{b}-\mathbf{a}) = \frac{3}{4}\mathbf{a}+\frac{1}{4}\mathbf{b} = \frac{1}{4}(3\mathbf{a}+\mathbf{b})$.

b) i) Position vector of B given by $\begin{pmatrix}5\\3\end{pmatrix}+\begin{pmatrix}-2\\1\end{pmatrix} = \begin{pmatrix}3\\4\end{pmatrix}$,

hence co-ordinate of B is (3,4).

ii) Modulus of $\overrightarrow{AB} = \sqrt{(2^2+1^2)} = \sqrt{5} = 2.24$.

iii) $\overrightarrow{AB} = \begin{pmatrix}-2\\1\end{pmatrix}$ then $\overrightarrow{BA} = \begin{pmatrix}2\\-1\end{pmatrix}$, hence $\overrightarrow{OR} = \begin{pmatrix}2\\-1\end{pmatrix}$, so co-ordinate of R will be (2, −1).

c) $k\begin{pmatrix}5\\3\end{pmatrix}+l\begin{pmatrix}1\\1\end{pmatrix} = \begin{pmatrix}8\\2\end{pmatrix} \rightarrow \begin{matrix} 5k+l = 8 \\ 3k+l = 2 \end{matrix}$

Solve simultaneously to give $k = 3, l = -7$.

A STUDENT'S ANSWER
WITH EXAMINER'S COMMENTS

Question

The vertices of a rectangle OABC are O(0,0), A(5,0), B(5,2) and C(0,2).

a)   Taking 1 cm to represent 1 unit on each axis and marking each axis from −6 to 6 draw
and label the rectangle OABC.   (2)

b)   The rectangle OABC is mapped onto rectangle $OA_1B_1C_1$ by the transformation
represented by the matrix **P** where

$$\mathbf{P} = \begin{pmatrix} 0 & 1 \\ 1 & 0 \end{pmatrix}.$$

Draw and label rectangle $OA_1B_1C_1$ on your diagram, and describe the transformation
fully in geometrical terms.   (3)

c)   The original rectangle OABC is mapped onto another rectangle $OA_2B_2C_2$ by reflection
in the x-axis. Draw and label the rectangle $OA_2B_2C_2$ on your diagram. Write down the
matrix **Q** which represents this transformation.   (3)

d)   The rectangle $OA_1B_1C_1$ can be mapped onto the rectangle $OA_2B_2C_2$ by a single
transformation represented by matrix **R**. Describe this transformation fully in
geometrical terms and state the relationship between the matrices **P, Q, R**.   (3)

e)   Find the smallest positive integer n for which $\mathbf{R}^n = \mathbf{I}$, where **I** is the identity
matrix.   (2)

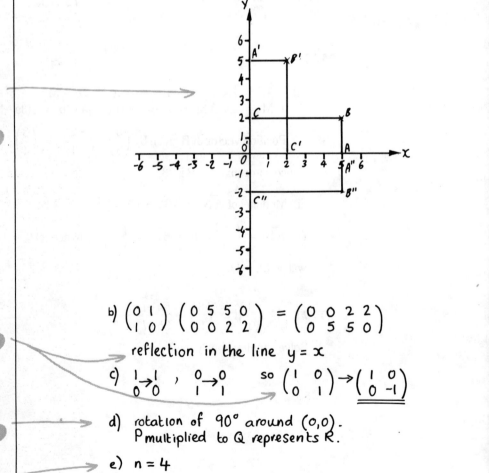

> **Good, clear
> diagram and well
> labelled, though you
> might have used the
> notation of the
> question!**

> **Correct and method of
> solution also good to
> show.**

b) $\begin{pmatrix} 0 & 1 \\ 1 & 0 \end{pmatrix} \begin{pmatrix} 0 & 5 & 5 & 0 \\ 0 & 0 & 2 & 2 \end{pmatrix} = \begin{pmatrix} 0 & 0 & 2 & 2 \\ 0 & 5 & 5 & 0 \end{pmatrix}$

reflection in the line $y = x$

> **The rotation would have
> been clearer as 90°
> anticlockwise (but it is still
> correct).**

c) $\begin{matrix} 1 \to 1 \\ 0 \to 0 \end{matrix}$, $\begin{matrix} 0 \to 0 \\ 1 \to 1 \end{matrix}$ so $\begin{pmatrix} 1 & 0 \\ 0 & 1 \end{pmatrix} \to \begin{pmatrix} 1 & 0 \\ 0 & -1 \end{pmatrix}$

d) rotation of 90° around (0,0).
P multiplied to Q represents R.

> **It would help if you could
> show how you got to this
> answer.**

e) $n = 4$

A good clear answer should get almost full marks, except for missing out
on the last part.

PROBABILITY AND STATISTICS

AVERAGE

ILLUSTRATING DATA

CUMULATIVE FREQUENCY

PROBABILITY AND EXPECTATION

GETTING STARTED

At the Higher level of GCSE mathematics, probability and statistics vary quite a bit as to what is in each syllabus, so do look up in chapter 2 the statistical content that you need.

You must be able to read and construct charts and graphs in order to find out information. You may well be asked to draw conclusions from the statistics that you are faced with.

USEFUL DEFINITIONS

Bar chart	A histogram with equal intervals, but may include a space between bars.
Continuous data	Data that when measured is usually rounded off.
Cumulative	Increasing by successive additions.
Discrete data	Data that can be identified by a single number.
Frequency	The number of times some defined event occurs.
Histogram	A chart with rectangular bars whose area is proportional to the frequency. Often the width of the bars will be different.
Mean	The result of adding together n items of data, then dividing by n.
Median	The middle item of data once the data has been put into order.
Mode	The item of data which occurs most frequently.
Ogive	The line representing cumulative frequency on a graph.
Pictogram	A display of information using pictures to represent the frequency.
Pie chart	A circular picture divided in the ratio of the frequencies it is illustrating.

ESSENTIAL PRINCIPLES

1 > **AVERAGE**

You need to know how to calculate the mode, median and mean from a *frequency distribution*. Now from a given list of data this is usually no problem. It is when we have *grouped* frequency and need to estimate our averages that the fun begins!

GROUPED FREQUENCY

Score	Frequency
0–20	8
21–40	15
41–60	36
61–80	27
81–100	14

Fig. 12.1

Suppose we are told the information in Fig. 12.1 about a maths exam, and the scores that the 5th year had obtained.

We can tell straight away that the *modal group* is 41–60. We have no way of estimating the modal individual score, without drawing a bar chart.

Estimating the median

This can be done in a number of ways. One is by using a cumulative graph and this will be fully explained in the later part of this chapter dealing with cumulative frequency. The other way is to do a 'linear interpolation', estimating where the median item of data is within its group. Here, we assume that items are spread evenly along any group (or class interval).

For the example given, the median item is the $(100+1)/2 = 50\frac{1}{2}$th item of data. We need to find a score corresponding to that item. Just evaluate the cumulative frequency here as 8, 23, 59 . . . until you get beyond the median ($50\frac{1}{2}$). Now we say that the median is

$$\frac{(50\frac{1}{2}-23)}{(59-23)}\times(60-41)+41 \ = \ 55.51 \text{ or } 56.$$

What we have done is to work out what *fraction of the way along the group* (41−60) the median is:

hence $\dfrac{50\frac{1}{2}-23}{59-23}$ works out this fraction of $(60-41)$,

Which is then added onto the *lowest value* of that group.

NB. Be careful with *continuous data*, since the lowest value of the group is often found *halfway between* the bottom value of that group and the top of the previous group.

Estimating the mean

This can be done by assuming that each person scored the middle mark of the group they are in, then calculating the total estimated scores and hence the mean. The table of values to do this will be as in Fig. 12.2.

❝❝Notice how the midway is found by adding each 'end score' and dividing by 2. Check it.**❞❞**

Score	Midway (m)	Frequency (f)	m x f
0–20	10	8	80
21–40	30.5	15	457.5
41–60	50.5	36	1818
61–80	70.5	27	1903.5
81–100	90.5	14	1267
	Totals	100	5526

Fig. 12.2

So the estimated mean is $5526 \div 100$, which is 55.26 or 55.

2 > **ILLUSTRATING DATA**

You need to be familiar with bar charts and pictograms, but it is unlikely that you will have questions involving these at this high level of GCSE mathematics.

PIE CHARTS

You could well be asked to interpret information from, or construct, a *pie chart*. You should be familiar with this, but do follow through the two worked examples.

WORKED EXAMPLE 1

The 'average family' split their net income in the way indicated in the pie chart in Fig. 12.3. Malcolm had an average family who one month spent £56 on clothes. Calculate i) How much they spent on leisure that month; ii) How much their net income was that month.

i) $£\dfrac{56}{24} \times 136 = £317.33$

(Notice we do it by simple proportions.)

ii) $£\dfrac{56}{24} \times 360 = £840.$

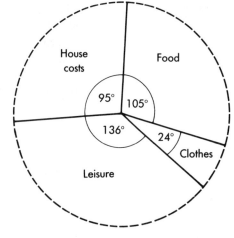

Fig. 12.3

WORKED EXAMPLE 2

A simple survey was done on the supporters of 'Sheffield Wednesday' and it was found to show the following age distribution of people present at one particular match:

    Under 16   . . . 5770
    Over 60   . . . 9800
    The rest   . . . 16,450

Present this information on a Pie Chart. Build up a table to evaluate the angles of the chart, as in Fig. 12.4.

Age	Frequency	Angle
Under 16	5770	$\dfrac{5770}{32020} \times 360 = 65°$
Over 60	9800	$\dfrac{9800}{32020} \times 360 = 110°$
the Rest	16450	$\dfrac{16450}{32020} \times 360 = 185°$
Totals	32020	360°

Fig. 12.4

This now needs drawing, starting with the smallest angles first, as in Fig. 12.5.

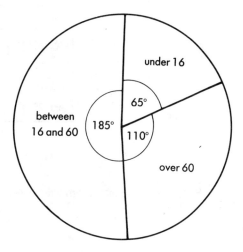

Fig. 12.5

HISTOGRAMS

A *histogram* looks similar to a *bar chart* inasmuch as it consists of bars to represent groups of data. However, the difference lies in the fact that it is the **area** of a bar in a histogram that represents the frequency; also the vertical axis will be a frequency density and not just the frequency.

Histograms are often used when one particular group is very large, so that a chart can be drawn that does at least represent the other, less important, data. For example, the histogram in Fig. 12.6 illustrates the age distribution of people regularly attending first division football matches at Hillsborough. To find out, for example, the frequency of the group 20–50, we multiply the f.d. (frequency density) of 500 by the group width of 30, to get 15 000; Similarly, the frequency of the 60–65 group will be the f.d. of 300 multiplied by 5 to give 1500.

In an examination question you will not normally be left to work out your own frequency density, it will usually be given to you. All you then need to make certain you remember is that (width of group)×f.d. = frequency.

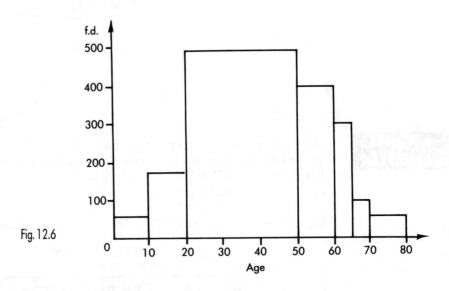

Fig. 12.6

Put the information in Fig. 12.7, about how long Dr. K. Speed took over examining his patients one week, into a histogram. The times are to the nearest minute.

Due to the continuous nature of the data and the size of the numbers, then the groups will need to be drawn on the graph to give bars of the following widths;

  0–2.5, 2.5–5.5, 5.5–10.5, 10.5–20 with widths of:
    2.5 ,   3 ,   5 ,   9.5

Since the area of the bars represents the frequency, then the height of each bar is given in Fig. 12.8.

Time Taken (minutes)	Frequency
0–2	8
3–5	15
6–10	36
11–20	57

Fig. 12.7

Group	Width	Frequency	Height
0–2	2.5	8	8÷2.5=3.2
3–5	3	15	15÷3=5.0
6–10	5	36	36÷5=7.2
10–20	9.5	57	57÷9.5=6.0

Fig. 12.8

So the accurate histogram will be as in Fig. 12.9.

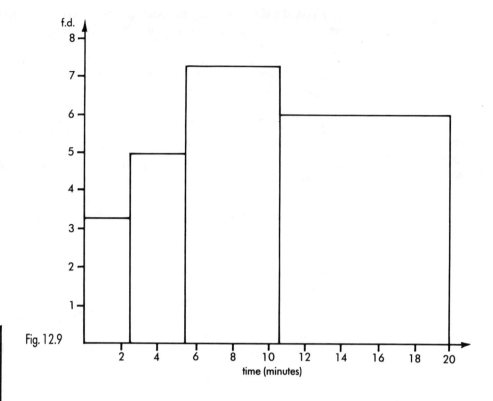

Fig. 12.9

Hours	Frequency
0–1	3
2–5	8
6–11	15
12–16	5

Fig. 12.10

EXERCISE 1

Work out the f.d. and heights of each bar in a histogram made from the information in Fig. 12.10 about the hours of sunshine during August in Bude in 1988.

3 > CUMULATIVE FREQUENCY

If it is on your syllabus then there is a very good chance that you will find a question on *cumulative frequency*. It is usually used to create an 'ogive', which is the graph you get if you graph the cumulative frequency. From this ogive you can estimate the median as well as quartiles and percentiles.

It is often called a running total, since that indeed is how the cumulative frequency is calculated. Follow through the example below to see how we draw the graph and how we find information from it.

On September 5th 1988, all the pupils in Pope Pius X School were measured in height to the nearest centimetre; Fig. 12.11 illustrates the distribution.

Heights (cm)	frequency (f)	cumulative frequency (cf)
115–120	6	6
121–130	30	36
131–140	85	121
141–150	160	281
151–160	180	461
161–170	41	502
171–175	2	504

Fig. 12.11

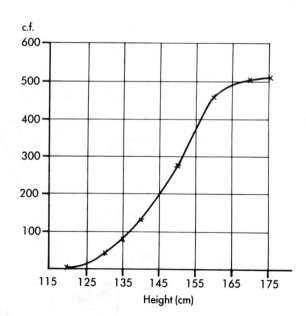

The cumulative frequency has been graphed against the height to give the ogive. Notice its distinctive shape and that the cumulative frequency (c.f.) is on the vertical axis, as it should always be.

We can estimate information such as 'How many pupils were over 165 cm.' We look at the c.f. for 165 cm by reading up, then along to 490, then we know that $504 - 490 = 14$, representing 14 pupils over 165 cm.

> **Do draw the graphs carefully and accurately as you may need to read information from them.**

ESTIMATING THE MEDIAN

From the c.f., find the middle item of data, where n is the total of the c.f., then the median is found by reading along, from $(n+1)/2$ on the c.f., to the ogive and down.

When we have large numbers, as in our example of 504, then it is often just as good to use the $n/2$ on the c.f. Here, the estimated median can be found by reading along from 252 on the c.f. to the ogive and down, to give the estimated median as 148.5 cm.

QUARTILES

Quartiles are found by dividing the c.f. into quarters and finding the 'quarter' marks. There are three divisions of the c.f. if we quarter it. The first one, the *lower* quartile is found by reading along from $\frac{1}{4}(n+1)$ on the c.f. The second one is the *median*, and the third is the *upper* quartile found by reading along from $\frac{3}{4}(n+1)$. Again, for large n you would round off to the nearest suitable integer to read on the c.f.

So for our example already given, we will have quartiles as in Fig. 12.12.

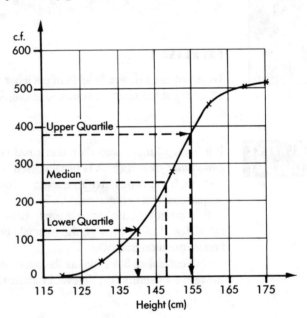

Fig. 12.12

$\frac{1}{4}(504) \rightarrow 126$ on c.f. to give lower quartile of 140.5 cm.
$\frac{3}{4}(504) \rightarrow 378$ on c.f. to give upper quartile of 154.5 cm.

THE INTERQUARTILE RANGE

This is the difference between the upper quartile and the lower quartile, and is expressed simply as this difference. Hence for our example above, the interquartile range is $154.5 - 140.5 = 14$ cm.

This range is useful to see how well the frequency is dispersed, as is the 'semi-interquartile range' which is simply half of the interquartile range!

EXERCISE 2

Find the semi-interquartile range, and estimate the median for the distribution of the weights of boxes of chocolates that were supposed to be 200 g, shown in Fig. 12.13.

Fig. 12.13

Weight (g)	−196	−197	−198	−199	−200	−201	−202	−203	−204
Frequency	6	23	35	50	65	44	36	32	9

4 > **PROBABILITY AND EXPECTATION**

"You need to be able to work out fractions with probability, you'll score few marks if you can't."

COMBINED EVENTS

Combined events are where two or more events are being combined in some way. When this happens we need to be aware of whether the events are dependent, independent, happening at the same time, or maybe one can happen without the other. We need to consider two main situations 'AND' and 'OR'.

AND

AND is the type where two or more events happen at the same time. You need to multiply together each probability.

WORKED EXAMPLE 4

Find the probability of tossing a coin 10 times and getting a head each time.

The chance of tossing a head is $\frac{1}{2}$ each time, hence for ten heads in a row, calculate $\frac{1}{2} \times \frac{1}{2} \times \frac{1}{2} \ldots$ (ten times) which is $(\frac{1}{2})^{10} = 9.8 \times 10^{-4}$.

EXERCISE 3

Calculate the probability of dealing four cards face up on the table and each one being an Ace.

OR

OR is the type when either one event *or* the other *or* both occur. In this case we must add together the probabilities. This only makes sense, however, in a situation where all the possible combinations have been considered.

WORKED EXAMPLE 5

Find the probability of cutting a pack of cards and finding a king or a queen.

The probability of a king is $\frac{1}{13}$, of a queen is $\frac{1}{13}$ and they cannot both happen at the same time, hence the probability of cutting one or the other is $\frac{1}{13} + \frac{1}{13} = \frac{2}{13}$.

AND and OR

This is how many of your examination problems are going to come, in situations where you need a combination of AND and OR.

WORKED EXAMPLE 6

The probability of Paul getting to school on time is 0.95. The probability of Michael being late for school is 0.1. What is the probability on any one day that either Paul or Michael (or both) are late for school?

The events that we can have are:

A : Paul late AND Michael not late.
B : Paul not late AND Michael late.
C : Paul late AND Michael late.

As the probability of Paul not being late is 0.95, the probability that he is late is $(1 - 0.95) = 0.05$.
As the probability of Michael being late is 0.1, the probability that he is not late is $(1 - 0.1) = 0.9$.

Hence the P(A) $= 0.05 \times 0.9 = 0.045$
           P(B) $= 0.95 \times 0.1 = 0.095$
           P(C) $= 0.05 \times 0.1 = 0.005$.

As we can have A OR B OR C, then add the probabilities to give

$$P(A) + P(B) + P(C) = 0.145.$$

Note: The last worked example illustrated the way in which AND and OR can be combined together, but for that example there is a quicker way of getting to the final answer. That is to first find the probability of neither being late, i.e. Paul is on time AND Michael is on time. This is $0.95 \times 0.9 = 0.855$.

The probability that one or the other is late $= 1-$ the probability of both not being late $= 1-0.855 = 0.145$.

As you see, this way is much quicker – if you spot it.

TREE DIAGRAMS

Tree diagrams are useful to illustrate some situations, but are often misused, and in fact used quite unnecessarily in many questions! If you can see what parts you need to get through a probability question then only use a tree diagram if you are specifically told to:

WORKED EXAMPLE 7

When Brian goes to Wales for his holiday he reckons that the chances of a hold up on the motorway are:

on the M1 a probability of 0.4, and
on the M50 a probability of 0.05.

What are the chances of his being held up on the motorways on his holiday to Wales? Here we can illustrate the chances on a tree diagram, as in Fig. 12.14.

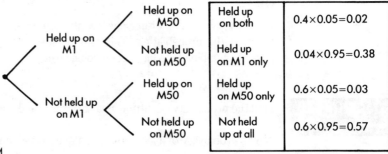

Fig. 12.14

NB. In this situation we were not asked for any one or two probabilities, but for all of them. Hence the tree diagram was useful to do this. Note also that all the final probabilities add up to 1.

WORKED EXAMPLE 8

In a group of 12 men and 9 women, two of them only are known to be Welsh. What is the probability that they are both of the same sex?

This problem, as far as we can tell, then is about choosing, at random, two people and them being of the same sex.

Here we either choose:

$$\text{man} \quad \text{then man} \qquad \therefore \frac{12}{21} \times \frac{11}{20} = \frac{132}{420}$$

$$\text{or woman then woman} \qquad \therefore \frac{9}{21} \times \frac{8}{20} = \frac{72}{420}$$

(Note how the second fraction is changed by the first one.)

Hence both the same sex has a chance of $\dfrac{132+72}{420} = \dfrac{204}{420}$.

EXERCISE 4

In a bag of sweets there are 10 chocolates, 5 jellies and 6 mints. Find the probability of taking out any two sweets and them both being different.

EXPECTATION

One of the main uses of probability is that of predicting some *expected* results. The expected number of times that event A will happen is found by multiplying the probability of A by the number of times the event has the opportunity of happening.

The A.A. reckon that any car taken at random has a probability of 0.004 of breaking down. They estimate that on August Bank Holiday there are 300 000 cars using the motorway networks. If they tried to have one patrol car for every 25 breakdowns, then how many patrol cars should they use on August Bank Holiday?

The expected number of breakdowns is $0.004 \times 300\ 000$ which is 1200. So the number of patrol cars will be $1200 \div 25 = 48$.

SOLUTIONS TO EXERCISES

S1

The table in Fig. 12.15 should help you to see if you have a correct histogram.

Hours	Width	f	Height on f.d.
0–1	1.5	3	$3 \div 1.5 = 2$
2–5	4	8	$8 \div 4 = 2$
6–11	6	15	$15 \div 6 = 2.5$
12–16	4.5	5	$5 \div 4.5 = 1.1$ (Rounded off)

Fig. 12.15

Hence the heights of your graph should be representative of the heights in this table.

S2

You need a cumulative frequency and graph, as: in Fig. 12.16.

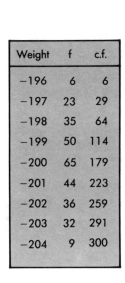

Weight	f	c.f.
−196	6	6
−197	23	29
−198	35	64
−199	50	114
−200	65	179
−201	44	223
−202	36	259
−203	32	291
−204	9	300

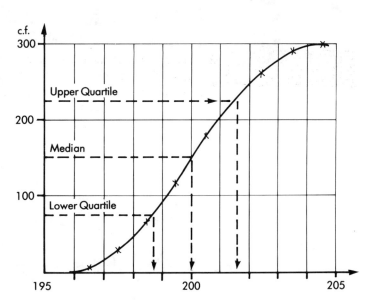

Fig. 12.16

Note where we've plotted the points, using 196.5, 197.5 . . . on the horizontal axis as being the most accurate figure for the c.f. due to the giving of information to the nearest gram and rounding off. This is necessary where you can tell this difference easily on the graph.

Look on the $(301) \times \frac{1}{4}$th for the lower quartile, which is $75.25 \rightarrow 198.75$ g
Look on the $(301) \times \frac{3}{4}$th for the upper quartile, which is $225.75 \rightarrow 201.6$ g
Hence the semi-interquartile range is $(201.6 - 198.75) \div 2 = 1.425$ g.
Look on the $(301)/2$th for the median, which is $150.5 \rightarrow 200$ g.

S3

The probability of the first card being an Ace is $\dfrac{4}{52}$.

The probability of the second being an Ace, given the first is an Ace, is $\dfrac{3}{51}$.

The probability of the third being an Ace, given the first two are Aces, is $\dfrac{2}{50}$.

Hence of the fourth being an Ace is . . . $\dfrac{1}{49}$.

Hence the probability that all 4 are Aces is:

$$\frac{4}{52} \times \frac{3}{51} \times \frac{2}{50} \times \frac{1}{49} \ = \ 3.7 \times 10^{-6}.$$

S4

The probability is $1-$(both being the same)
The probability both being the same is given by:

P(both chocolate)+P(both jellies)+P(both mints),

$$\left(\frac{10}{21} \times \frac{9}{20}\right) \ + \ \left(\frac{5}{21} \times \frac{4}{20}\right) \ + \ \left(\frac{6}{21} \times \frac{5}{20}\right)$$

which is $\dfrac{90+20+30}{21 \times 20}$

which is $140/420 \ = \ \dfrac{1}{3}$.

Hence the chance of both being different is $1-\dfrac{1}{3}$ which is $\dfrac{2}{3}$.

EXAMINATION TYPE QUESTIONS

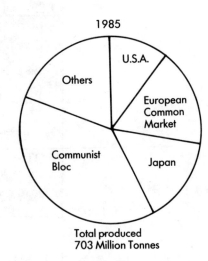

Fig. 12.17

Q1

The pie charts in Fig. 12.17 indicate the proportion of steel produced in the world by various economies in 1974 and 1985.
Use these diagrams to answer the following questions.

a)   Which economies did not improve their world proportion from 1974 to 1985?

b) i) Measure and state the angle of the sector representing the European Common Market in 1974.

  ii) How many tonnes of steel did the European Common Market produce in 1974?

c) Calculate the percentage increase of the Communist Bloc's proportion of steel production from 1974 to 1985. (NEA; 1988)

Q2

Mrs. McAllister, an agent for a firm, kept a record of the time she spent (including travelling) on each customer she saw. During one particular 5 day week, she saw 80 customers and the record of the times spent on them is summarised in Fig. 12.18.

Fig. 12.18

Time (*t* minutes)	20<*t*≤25	25<*t*≤30	30<*t*≤35	35<*t*≤40	40<*t*≤45	45<*t*≤50
Number of customers	8	10	10	30	18	4

a) Find the mean number of customers Mrs. McAllister saw per day during this week.

b) Mrs. McAllister's normal working week is 40 hours. Calculate an estimate of the number of hours overtime which she worked during this week.

c) Calculate an estimate of the mean length of time Mrs. McAllister spent per customer.

d) On graph paper, draw a cumulative frequency diagram for this distribution.

e) Use your diagram to estimate

  i) the interquartile range for this distribution

  ii) the number of customers on each of whom Mrs. McAllister spent more than the mean length of time found in part c). (MEG; 1988)

Q3

The number of full-time female students in the U.K. in 1981 in various age groups is shown in Fig. 12.19. (Frequencies are given to the nearest thousand.)

Fig. 12.19

Age (years)	16–	20–	25–	35–	45–54	Total
No. (in thousands)	672	139	34	13	4	862

a) This information is to be represented in a histogram using a scale of 2 cm to represent 5 years on the age axis and 4 cm² to represent 100 thousand students. Given that the width of the first rectangle is 1.6 cm, calculate its height.

b) Draw the histogram.

c) By using mid-interval values, estimate the mean age of female students, giving your answer correct to the nearest tenth of a year. (NEA; 1988)

Q4

A bag contains 5 red discs, 4 white discs and 1 blue disc. Two discs are to be chosen at random, without replacement.

a) Complete the probability tree diagram in Fig. 12.20.

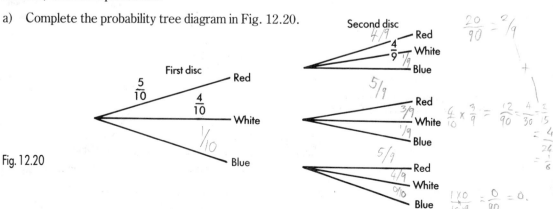

Fig. 12.20

b) Find the probability that
    i) both dics will be red,
    ii) both discs will be blue,
    iii) both discs will be the same colour,
    iv) the two discs will be different colours.   (LEAG; 1988)

Q5

(Give the answers to this question as fractions in their lowest terms.)
In a game, one red dice and one blue dice are used. Both dice are unbiased, but the faces of
the red dice are numbered 1, 1, 2, 3, 4, 5 and the faces of the blue dice are numbered 1, 1,
2, 2, 4, 4.

a) The two dice are thrown together, find the probability of each of the following events:
    i) The score on the red dice is an odd number.
    ii) The score on the blue dice is greater than the score on the red dice.
    iii) The scores on the two dice are equal.

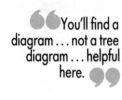 You'll find a
diagram ... not a tree
diagram ... helpful
here.

b) The two dice are thrown together on two occasions. Find the probability that the score
on the blue dice is greater than the score on the red dice on both occasions.
                                                    (MEG; 1988)

Q6

Part of a children's game involves rolling a normal 6-faced dice, then spinning an arrow as
shown in Fig. 12.21.
If on the spinner you get:

    a dice – you have another roll of the dice
    a spider – you choose a spider part
    a foot – you move on one space on a board
    a drink – you miss a go.

Fig. 12.21

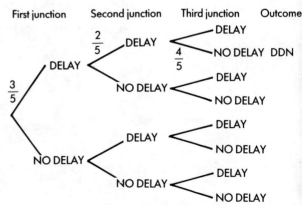

a) Find the probability of getting:
    i) a spider   ii) a foot;   iii) a drink.
b) To win a game on his next go, John had to
    either roll a 3 on the dice, then spin a spider
         or roll a 5 on the dice, then spin a foot.
    Calculate the probability that John will win on his next go.   (NEA; 1988)

Q7

Mr. Meiring travels to work by car on five days each week. He has to cross three busy
junctions. He finds that he is delayed three times a week at the first junction, twice a week
at the second junction, and once a week at the third junction. A delay at one junction does
not affect a delay at any other junction.

a) Complete the probability tree diagram in Fig. 12.22, using D for delay, and N for no
delay, in the Outcome column.

	First junction	Second junction	Third junction	Outcome
		$\frac{2}{5}$ DELAY	DELAY	
			$\frac{4}{5}$ NO DELAY	DDN
	$\frac{3}{5}$ DELAY		DELAY	
		NO DELAY	NO DELAY	
		DELAY	DELAY	
			NO DELAY	
	NO DELAY		DELAY	
		NO DELAY	NO DELAY	

Fig. 12.22

b) Find the probability that, on any morning he will,
   i) arrive at work without being delayed,
   ii) be delayed at only *one* of the three junctions. (LEAG; 1988)

Q8

A school entered 50 candidates for GCSE mathematics. There are two papers, each marked out of a maximum of 50. The marks obtained in Paper 1 are shown in Fig. 12.23 and illustrated by the frequency diagram.

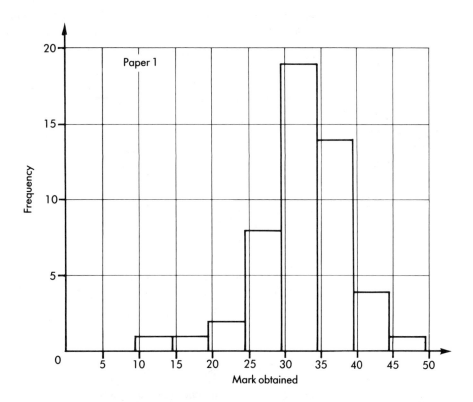

Fig. 12.23

Mark range	0–4	5–9	10–14	15–19	20–24	25–29	30–34	35–39	40–44	45–49
Number of candidates	0	0	1	1	2	8	19	14	4	1

a) Calculate an estimate of the mean mark obtained in Paper 1.
   The marks obtained in Paper 2 are shown in Fig. 12.24.

27	18	31	12	16	37	24	42	15	23
27	27	42	21	3	12	27	24	34	13
9	29	19	32	24	26	33	15	24	25
24	30	23	13	17	6	39	19	18	38
12	18	18	26	31	24	49	12	23	29

Fig. 12.24

b) Compile a frequency table for the marks in Paper 2. Use the same classes as Paper 1.
c) On graph paper, illustrate the data for Paper 2, using the same scales as the frequency diagram for Paper 1.
d) Comment briefly on the differences between the candidate's performances in the two papers. (You may like to use the fact that the mean mark for Paper 2 is 23.6.) (MEG; 1988)

Q9

When a biased 6-sided dice is thrown, a score of 6 is twice as likely as a score of 5; a score of 5 is twice as likely as a score of 4; and scores of 1, 2, 3, 4 are equally likely.
Calculate the probability of
- i) a score of 1
- ii) a score of 6
- iii) scoring an even number.   (NEA; 1988)

Q10

In a survey, 100 motorists were asked to record the petrol consumption of their cars in miles per gallon. Each figure was rounded to the nearest mile per gallon and the frequency distribution shown in Fig. 12.25 was obtained.

Fig. 12.25

Miles per gallon	26–30	31–35	36–40	41–45	46–50	51–55	56–60
Frequency	4	6	18	34	20	12	6

a) i) State the limits of the model class of this distribution.
   ii) Complete the 'less than' cumulative frequency table in Fig. 12.26:

Fig. 12.26

Miles per gallon (less than)	30.5	35.5	40.5	50.5	55.5	65.5
Number of motorists	4	10				

   iii) On graph paper, draw the cumulative frequency curve (ogive) from your completed cumulative frequency table.

b) Use your cumulative frequency curve to estimate:
   i) the median of the distribution
   ii) the interquartile range.

A 'good' petrol consumption is one which lies between 38 and 52 miles per gallon.

c) Estimate the number of motorists whose petrol consumption was 'good'.
                                                                              (NISEC; Specimen

EXTENSION   Q11

Five married couples are at a party.

a) Two people are chosen at random. Find the probability that
   i) they are a married couple,
   ii) one is a man and one is a woman,
   iii) at least one man is chosen.
b) Four people are chosen at random. Find the probability that
   i) three women and one man are chosen
   ii) no married couple is among the four.   (WJEC; 1988

Q12

Fig. 12.27

Date	Jan. 5	Feb. 16	Mar. 30	May 11	June 22	Aug. 3	Sept. 14	Oct. 26	Dec. 7
Daylight (hours–minutes)	8 h 01 m	10 h 03 m	12 h 48 m	15 h 23 m	16 h 40 m	15 h 19 m	12 h 46 m	10 h 03 m	8 h 02 m

The second line of the table in Fig. 12.27 gives the length of a 'day' in England (in hours and minutes of daylight) at six-weekly intervals from January 5th, 1985.

a) Complete the table in Fig. 12.28:

Number of weeks after Jan. 5 (x)	0	6								48
Daylight (hours) to one decimal place (y)	8.0	10.1							10.1	8

Fig. 12.28

b) Using scales of 0.2 cm to 1 week and 1 cm to 1 hour along the x and y axes respectively, draw a graph of y against x, joining your points with a smooth curve.

c) i) On the curve, mark the point corresponding to June 1st and label it J.

   ii) Find the hours of daylight on June 1st.

d) i) On your graph, mark the two points at which 'day' is equal to 'night'. Label the left-hand point A and the right-hand point B.

   ii) For how many weeks of the year is 'day' longer than 'night'?

   iii) Estimate the date corresponding to point A.   (O and C; 1986)

OUTLINE ANSWERS TO EXAM QUESTIONS

A1

a) The ones whose angles have got smaller: Japan, ECM and USA.

b) i) Any answer between 79° and 83° would be acceptable.

   ii) Your part i) answer $\times \dfrac{704}{360}$ = between 154 and 162 million.

c) Again, the angle measurement can be as much as 2° out, but if you were really accurate, the first angle is 107°, the second 138°, hence the proportional increase is $\dfrac{138-107}{107}$. To make this a percentage just multiply this answer by 100 to get 29%.

A2

a) $(8+10+10+30+18+4) \div 5 = 16$.

b) Figure 12.29 shows how to estimate the total time spent in minutes, which will be 47.7 hours (2860 mins÷60), so she spent approximately 8 hours overtime.

c) $2860 \div 80 = 35.75$ minutes. (36 would do.)

d) See Fig. 12.30.

Time	Halfway (m)	f	mxf
20–25	22.5	8	180
25–30	27.5	10	275
30–35	32.5	10	325
35–40	37.5	30	1125
40–45	42.5	18	765
45–50	47.5	4	190
	Totals	80	2860

Fig. 12.29

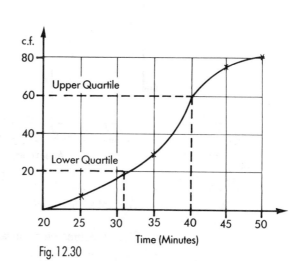

Fig. 12.30

e) i) Upper quartile $(\frac{3}{4}\times81)$th $=$ 40.5.
       Lower quartile $(\frac{1}{4}\times81)$th $=$ 31.
       Hence interquartile range $=$ 40.5−31 $=$ 9.5 minutes.
    ii) Mean length of 35.75 minutes.
       Read up to the ogive $=$ 33 people below this mark.
       So she would see (80−33) $=$ 47 customers longer than the estimated mean.

A3

a) To represent 672 thousand you need an area of $\frac{672}{100}\times4$ $=$ 26.88 cm³, so if

    width $=$ 1.6 cm, the height $=$ $\frac{26.88}{1.6}$ $=$ 16.8 cm.

b) The widths and heights of the other rectangles are given in Fig. 12.31.

Age	Width (cm)	f	Height (cm)
16–20	4×⅖=1.6	672	(672×0.04)÷1.6=16.8
20–25	5×⅖=2.0	139	(139×0.04)÷2.0=2.78
25–35	10×⅖=4.0	34	(34×0.04)÷4.0=0.34
35–45	10×⅖=4.0	13	(13×0.04)÷4.0=0.13
45–54	9×⅖=3.6	4	(4×0.04)÷3.6=0.04

Fig. 12.31

So your histogram should look like that in Fig. 12.32.

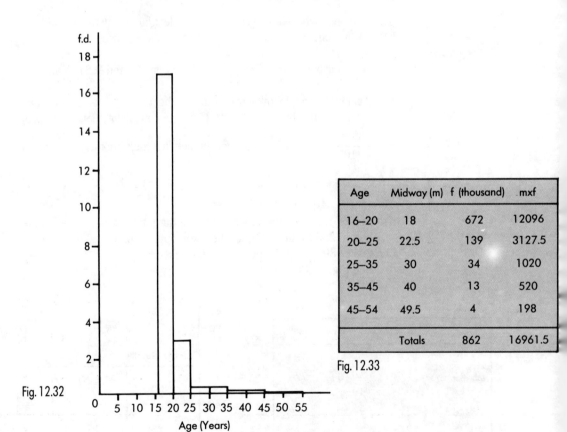

Fig. 12.32

Age	Midway (m)	f (thousand)	mxf
16–20	18	672	12096
20–25	22.5	139	3127.5
25–35	30	34	1020
35–45	40	13	520
45–54	49.5	4	198
	Totals	862	16961.5

Fig. 12.33

c) Your table to estimate this should look like Fig. 12.33.

    So your estimated mean will be 16961.5÷862 $=$ 19.7 years.

A4

a) See Fig. 12.34.

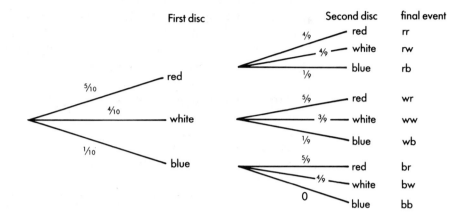

Fig. 12.34

b) i) $P(rr) = \dfrac{5}{10} \times \dfrac{4}{9} = \dfrac{20}{90} = \dfrac{2}{9}$.

ii) $P(bb) = \dfrac{1}{10} \times 0 = 0$.

iii) $P(\text{same colour}) = P(rr)+P(ww)+P(bb) = \dfrac{2}{9}+\dfrac{4}{10} \times \dfrac{3}{9}+0 = \dfrac{32}{90}$.

iv) $P(\text{different colours}) = 1-P(\text{same colour}) = 1-\dfrac{32}{90} = \dfrac{58}{90}$.

A5

a) i) $\dfrac{4}{6} = \dfrac{2}{3}$.

The best way to indicate all of the equally likely events to help you find the probability of combined events here is to sketch the following diagrams.

ii)

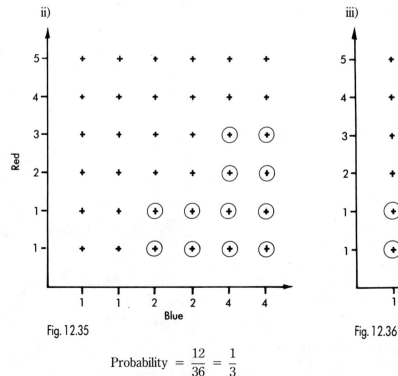

Fig. 12.35

Probability $= \dfrac{12}{36} = \dfrac{1}{3}$

iii)

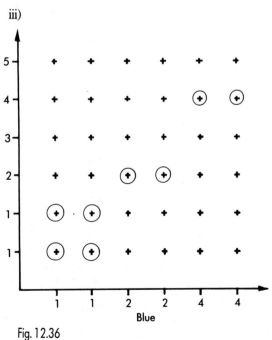

Fig. 12.36

Probability $= \dfrac{8}{36} = \dfrac{2}{9}$

b) $\dfrac{1}{3} \times \dfrac{1}{3} = \dfrac{1}{9}$.

A6

a) i) $\dfrac{5}{12}$; ii) $\dfrac{3}{12}$ or $\dfrac{1}{4}$; iii) $\dfrac{2}{12}$ or $\dfrac{1}{6}$.

b) A tree diagram may help you to visualise the whole situation, but is not the best method to solve this particular problem.

$$P(\text{roll 3 then spin a spider}) = \dfrac{1}{6} \times \dfrac{5}{12} = \dfrac{5}{72}$$

$$P(\text{roll 5 then spin a foot}) = \dfrac{1}{6} \times \dfrac{1}{4} = \dfrac{1}{24}$$

$$\text{Add them together to give } \dfrac{5}{72} + \dfrac{1}{24} = \dfrac{8}{72}$$

A7

a) See Fig. 12.37

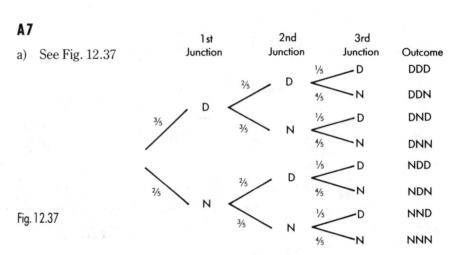

Fig. 12.37

b) i) $P(NNN) = \dfrac{2}{5} \times \dfrac{3}{5} \times \dfrac{4}{5} = \dfrac{24}{125}$

ii) $P(DNN) + P(NDN) + P(NND) = \left(\dfrac{3}{5} \cdot \dfrac{3}{5} \cdot \dfrac{4}{5}\right) + \left(\dfrac{2}{5} \cdot \dfrac{2}{5} \cdot \dfrac{4}{5}\right) + \left(\dfrac{2}{5} \cdot \dfrac{3}{5} \cdot \dfrac{1}{5}\right)$

$= \dfrac{36}{125} + \dfrac{16}{125} + \dfrac{6}{125} = \dfrac{58}{125}$

A8

a) Use the table of values as in Fig. 12.38:

Mark Range	Midway (m)	f	m x f
0–4	2	0	0
5–9	7	0	0
10–14	12	1	12
15–19	17	1	17
20–24	22	2	44
25–29	27	8	216
30–34	32	19	608
35–39	37	14	518
40–44	42	4	168
45–49	47	1	47
Totals		50	1630

Hence the estimated mean
$= 1630 \div 50 = 32.6$.

Fig. 12.38

b) You should have a table of values as in Fig. 12.39.

Mark Range	0–4	5–9	10–14	15–19	20–24	25–29	30–34	35–39	40–44	45–49
Number of Candidates	1	2	6	10	10	9	6	3	2	1

Fig. 12.39

c) You should have a diagram as in Fig. 12.40:

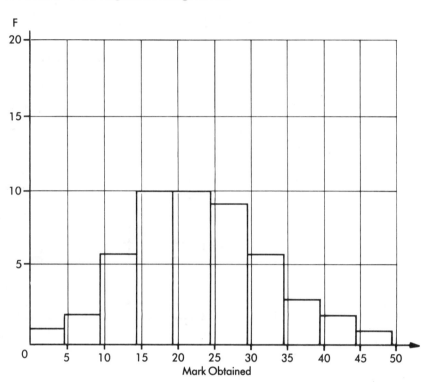

Fig. 12.40

d) They performed better on paper 1 than on paper 2 as the mean marks of 32.6 on paper 1 and 23.6 on paper 2 suggest. However, paper 2 has a better range and spread of marks than does paper 1. You could say that paper 1 was in good GCSE paper as most of the students gained over half marks, where paper 2 was not, as most of the students scored less than half marks.

A9

Let the probability of scoring a 4 be x, then the table in Fig. 12.41 illustrates each probability.

Score	1	2	3	4	5	6
Probability	x	x	x	x	$2x$	$4x$

Fig. 12.41

Hence where the total of the probabilities is 1, then $10x = 1$ and so $x = 0.1$,
hence i) $P(1) = 0.1$
ii) $P(6) = 0.4$
iii) $P(2 \text{ or } 4 \text{ or } 6) = 0.1 + 0.1 + 0.4 = 0.6$.

A10

a) i) Modal class is 41–50.
ii) See Fig. 12.42.

(Less than) Miles per gallon	30.5	35.5	40.5	45.5	50.5	55.5	60.5
No. of Motorists	4	10	28	62	82	94	100

Fig. 12.42

iii) You should have an ogive as in Fig. 12.43.

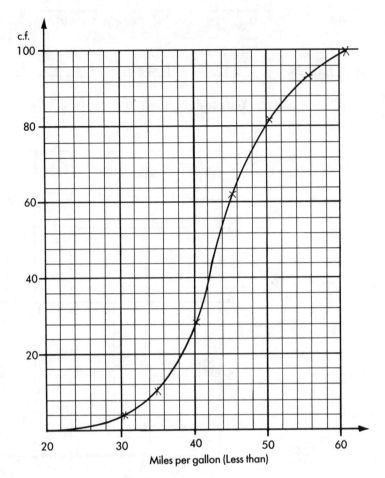

Fig. 12.43

b)   i) Median – read off the $(101)/2 = 50\frac{1}{2}$th on the c.f. to give 43.8 mpg.
    ii) Upper quartile read off the $(101)\times\frac{3}{4} = 75.75$th on the c.f. to give 48.5 mpg.
        Lower quartile read off the $(101)/4 = 25.25$th on the c.f. to give 40 mpg.
        Hence the interquartile range is $48.5-40 = 8.5$ mpg.
c)   Reading up to the ogive and hence the c.f. from 38 and 52 miles you get 17 and 86
     respectively. Hence the number of motorists in between this that have 'good' petrol
     consumption is $86-17 = 69$.

A11

a)   i) The first person can be anybody, then the probability that the next person is
        married to the first person will be $\frac{1}{9}$.

    ii) Can choose either 'man then woman' *or* 'woman then man', so the probability is
        $$P(MW)+P(WM) = \left(\frac{5}{10}\times\frac{5}{9}\right)+\left(\frac{5}{10}\times\frac{5}{9}\right) = \frac{50}{90}.$$

    iii) The quickest way is to find $1 - P(\text{no men})$.
        $$P(\text{no men}) = P(\text{women then women}) = \frac{5}{10}\times\frac{4}{9} = \frac{20}{90},$$
        hence answer $= 1-\frac{20}{90} = \frac{70}{90}.$

        The alternative is to choose either 'man then woman' *or* 'woman then man' *or* 'man
        then man', so the probability is $\frac{50}{90}+\left(\frac{5}{10}\times\frac{4}{9}\right) = \frac{70}{90}.$

b)   Choose either (WWWM) or (WWMW) or (WMWW) or (MWWW)
      i) which in effect is $4\times\left(\frac{5}{10}\times\frac{4}{9}\times\frac{3}{8}\times\frac{5}{7}\right) = 0.238$

ii) P(first person) = 1 it can be anybody

P (next person *not* married to first) = $\dfrac{8}{9}$

P(next person *not* married to either of first two) = $\dfrac{6}{8}$

P(next person *not* married to either of first three) = $\dfrac{4}{7}$

hence the probability is $1 \times \dfrac{8}{9} \times \dfrac{6}{8} \times \dfrac{4}{7}$ = 0.381.

A12

a) See Fig. 12.44.

Numbers of weeks after Jan. 5th (x)	0	6	12	18	24	30	36	42	48
Daylight (hours) to one decimal place	8.0	10.1	12.8	15.4	16.7	15.3	12.8	10.1	8.0

Fig. 12.44

b) See Fig. 12.45.

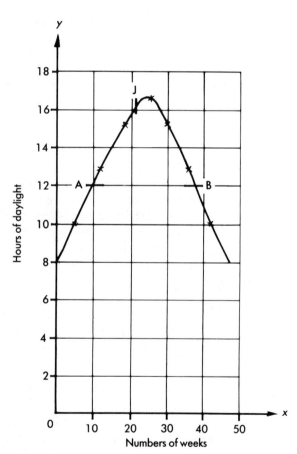

Fig. 12.45

c) i) June 1st is 21 weeks after January 5th.
    ii) Hours of daylight on June 1st = 16.3 = 16 hours 18 min.
d) i) See Fig. 12.45, points A and B.
    ii) This is the number of weeks between A and B, which is 28 weeks.
    iii) Point A is 10 weeks after January 5th, which is 70 days after January 5th, which corresponds to March 16th.

INDEX